Hanon Complete

The Virtuoso Pianist

In Sixty Exercises

by

Charles L. Hanon

Part 1.

Preparatory Exercises for Acquiring Agility, Independence, Strength and Perfect Evenness in the Fingers.

No. 1.

This exercise helps develop stretching between the fourth and fifth fingers of the left hand ascending, and the right hand descending. Fingers should be lifted high, and each note played distinctly, with precision. Begin all twenty exercises of Part 1 with the metronome set at M.M.60, and, with practice, gradually increase speed to M.M.108, as indicated by the double metronome mark.

C. L. Hanon

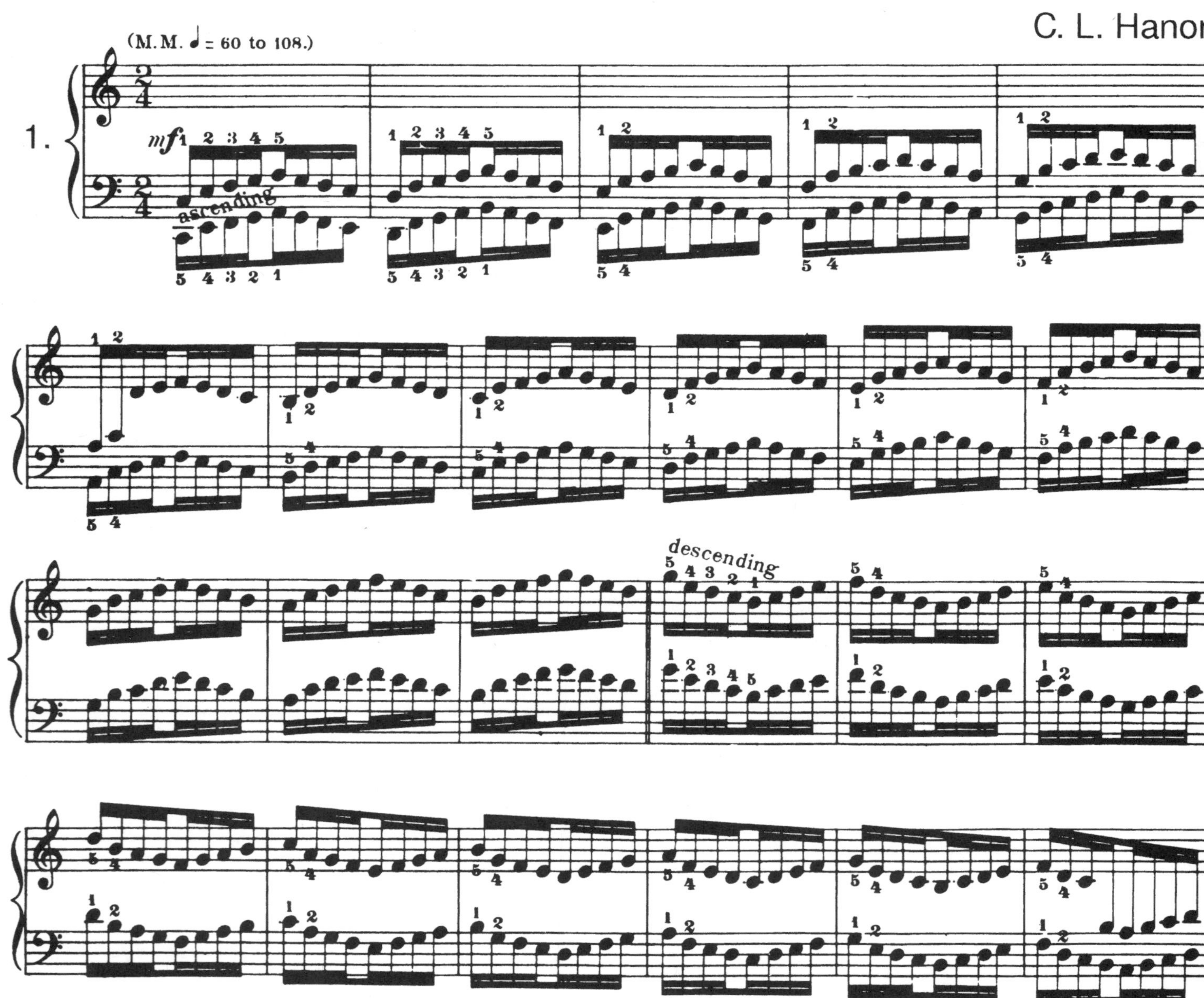

The numbers signify those fingers which are specifically trained in each exercise as shown at the beginning of each exercise. Both hands, the left hand ascending or the right hand descending, are constantly coping with the same difficulties and mastering these exercises will allow for the hands to develop perfect equality.

After mastering exercises 1. & 2., proceed from exercise 1. to exercise 2. omitting this measure.

No. 2

This exercise, and succeeding exercises to No. 31 are designed to make the 4th and 5th finger, which are naturally weak, as strong and agile as the second and third fingers. After mastering exercises No. 1 and No. 2, it is recommended to play four times together without stopping.

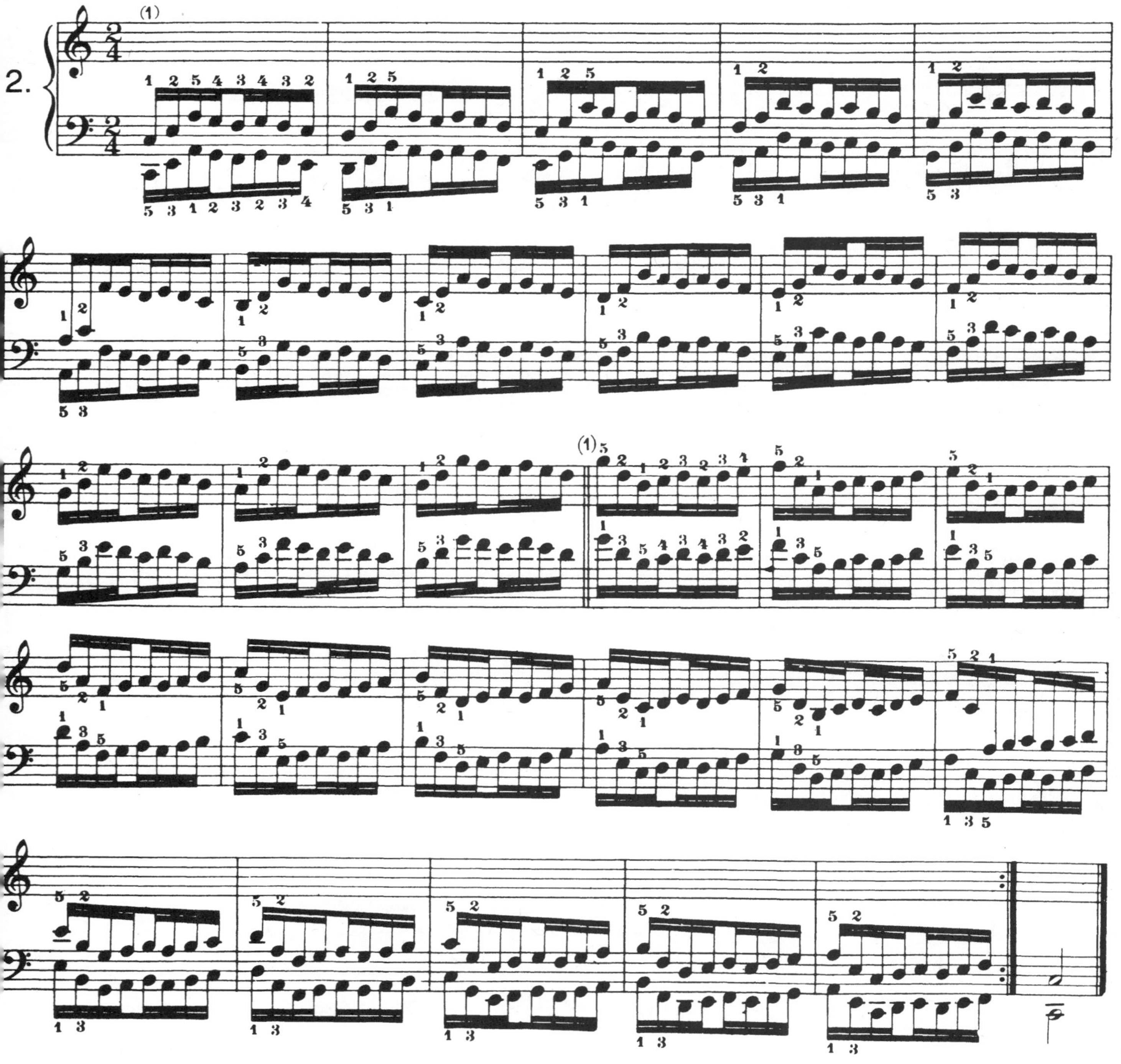

2.

No. 3

After mastering exercises No. 3, No. 4 and No. 5, they should be played together at least four times without stopping. The remaining exercises should be practiced in multiples of three, after they are mastered, so that in practicing, stop only at the last note on pages 3, 6, 9, 12, 15, 18, and 21.

No. 4

3-4-5 This exercise concentrates on the 3rd, 4th, and 5th fingers.

No. 5

1-2-3-4-5 This exercise is intended to perfect the trill with the 4th and 5th fingers of the right hand. (Remember to lift fingers high, play distinctly)

No. 6

5 For best results these exercises should be practiced daily.

No. 7.

3-4-5 This exercise is important for the development of the 3rd, 4th, and 5th fingers.

No. 8.

1-2-3-4-5 This exercise is very important for all five fingers.

No. 9.

1-2-3-4-5 This is a general exercise with emphasis on the extension of the 4th & 5th fingers.

No. 10.

3-4 This is a preliminary exercise for the trill of the 3rd and 4th fingers of both hands.

10.

No. 11.

3-4-5 This is a preliminary exercise for the trill of the 4th & 5th fingers.

No. 12.

1-2-3-4-5 This is an exercise for the extension of 1-5 fingers, and also an exercise for the 3rd, 4th, and 5th fingers.

No. 13.

No. 14.

3-4 This is another preliminary exercise for the trill for the 3rd and 4th fingers.

No. 15.

1-2 This is a general exercise for all five fingers, with special emphasis on the extension of 1st and 2nd fingers.

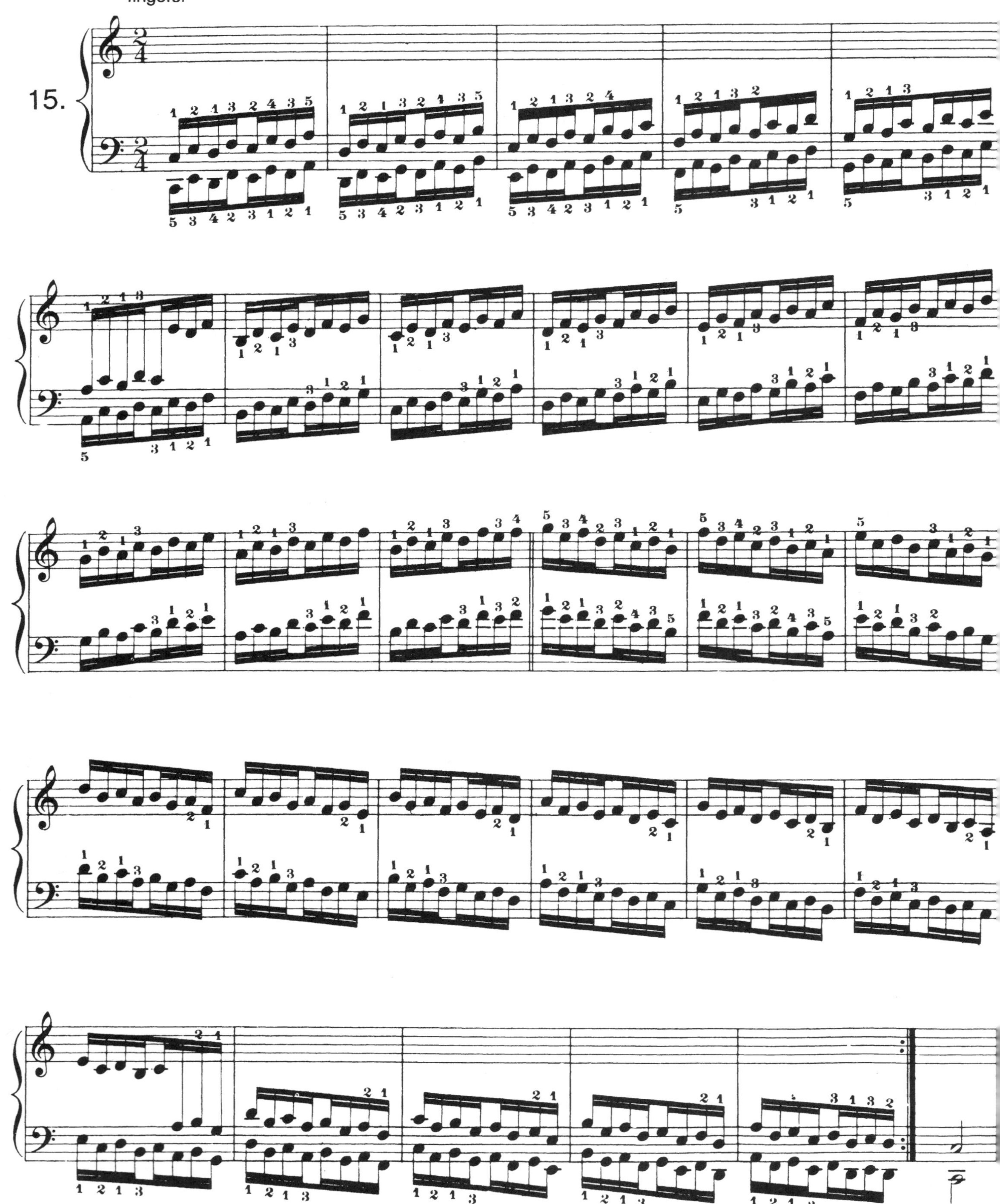

No. 16.

3-5 This is an exercise for the extension of 3rd and 5th fingers, and also an exercise for the 3rd, 4th, and 5th fingers.

No. 17.

1-2, 2-4, 4-5 This is an exercise for the extension of 1st and 2nd fingers, 2nd and 4th fingers, 4th and 5th fingers, and a general exercise for 3rd, 4th, and 5th fingers.

No. 18.

No. 19.

No. 20.

2-4, 4-5 This is an exercise for the extension of the 2nd and 4th fingers, 4th and 5th fingers, and exercises for the 2nd, 3rd, and 4th fingers.

End Of Part One

The complete mastery of part one is essential to undertaking a study of part two.

The Virtuoso Pianist Part 2.

Further Exercises Designed to Prepare the Fingers for Virtuoso Technic.

Note that what the 3rd, 4th, and 5th fingers of the left hand plays on the 1st beat of each measure (A), is repeated by the right hand on the 3rd beat of each measure (B).

C.L. Hano

As in part one, beginning all exercises in part two with the metronome set at M.M 60 and gradually increase to M.M. 108, unless otherwise indicated.

5 4 3 4 5 4 3 2 1
1 2 3 2 1 2 3 4 5
After mastering exercises 21 & 22, proceed from exercises 21 to 22 without stopping on this note.

No. 22

3-4-5 This exercise, as in No. 21, concentrates on the 3rd, 4th, and 5th fingers.

The remaining exercises should be played in groups, with stopping only on the last note on pages 24, 29, 33, 37, 41, 44, 46, and 49.

No. 23

No. 24

No. 25

No. 26

No. 27

1-2-3-4-5 This exercise prepares the 4th and 5th fingers for the trill given further on.

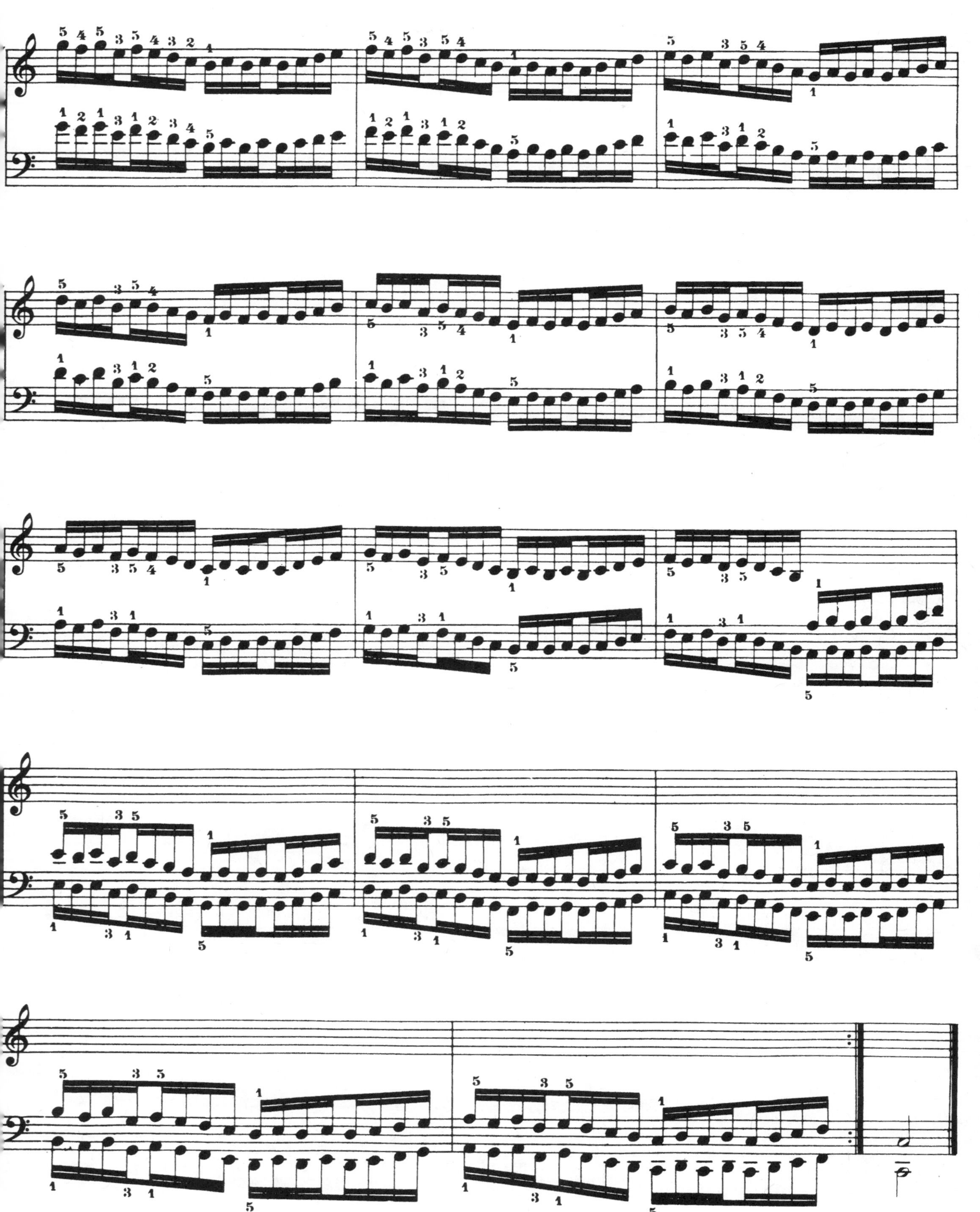

No. 28

No. 29

1-2-3-4-5 This is a trill exercise for all five fingers.

No. 30

1-2-4-5 This is a trill exercise for the 1st and 2nd fingers, and the 4th and 5th fingers.

No. 31

1-2-3-4-5 (and extensions)

Turning The Thumb Under

Turning the thumb under the 2nd finger.

M. M. 𝅗𝅥 = 40 to 72.

Repeat this measure 4 times

32.

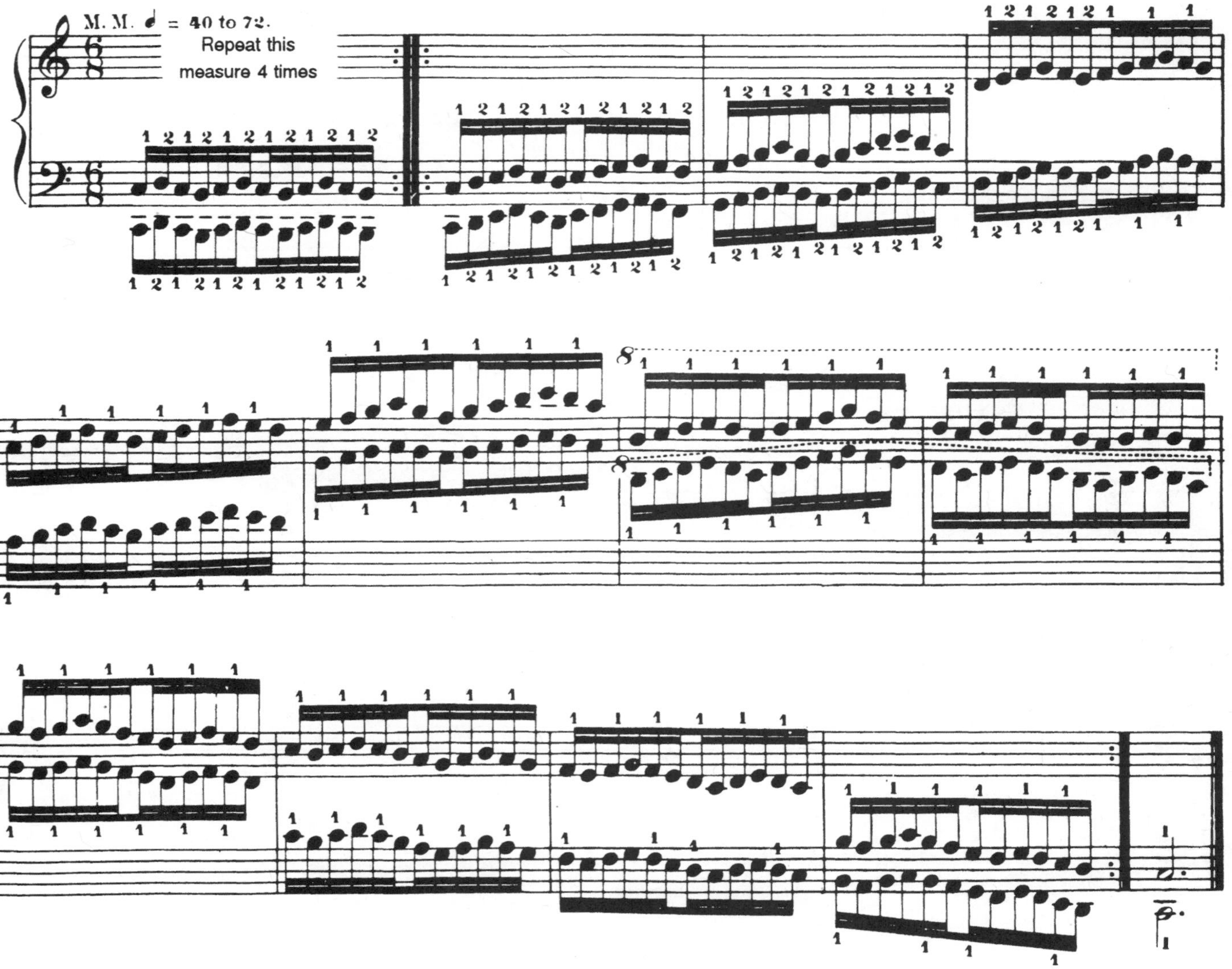

Turning the thumb under the 3rd finger.

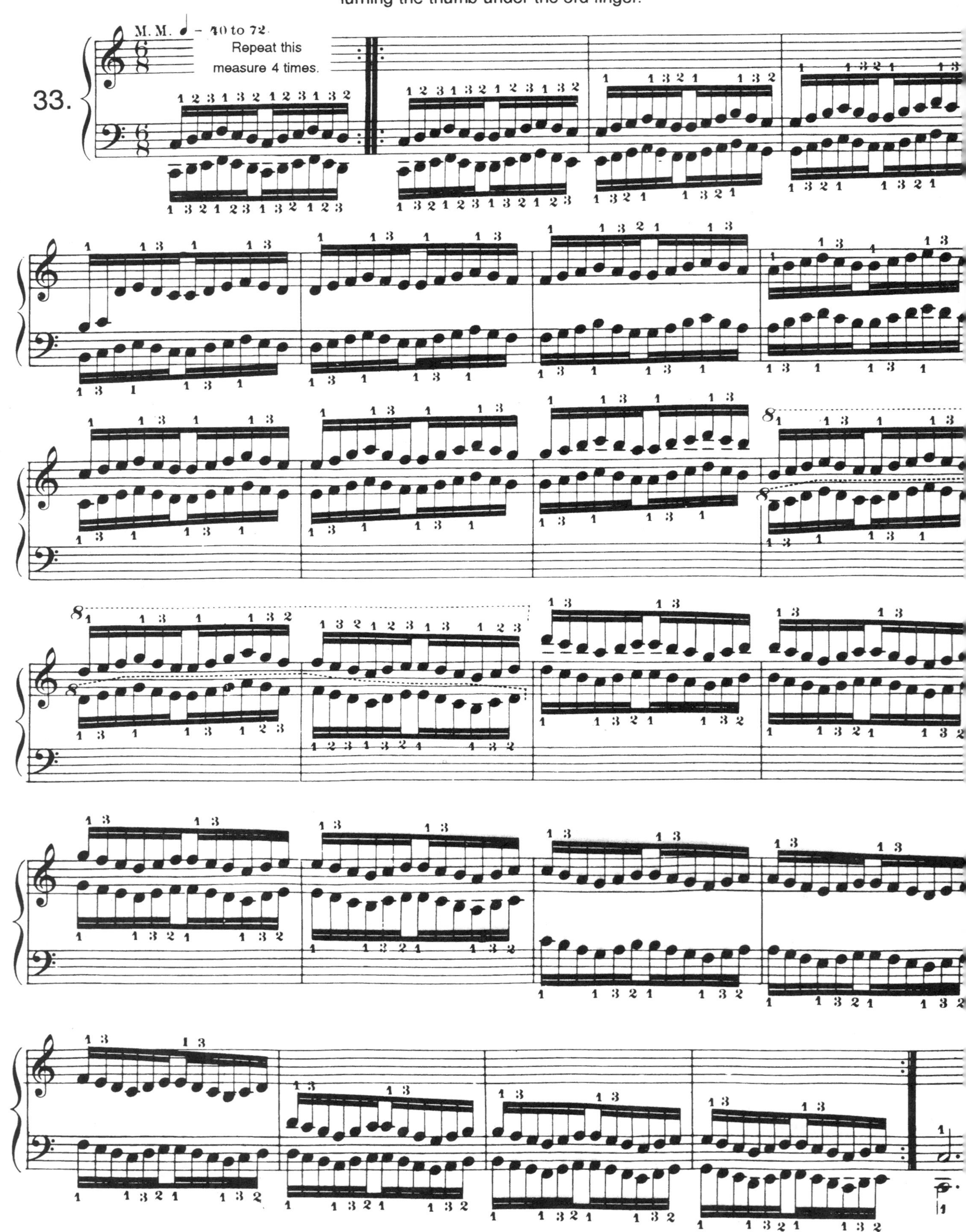

Turning the thumb under the 4th finger.

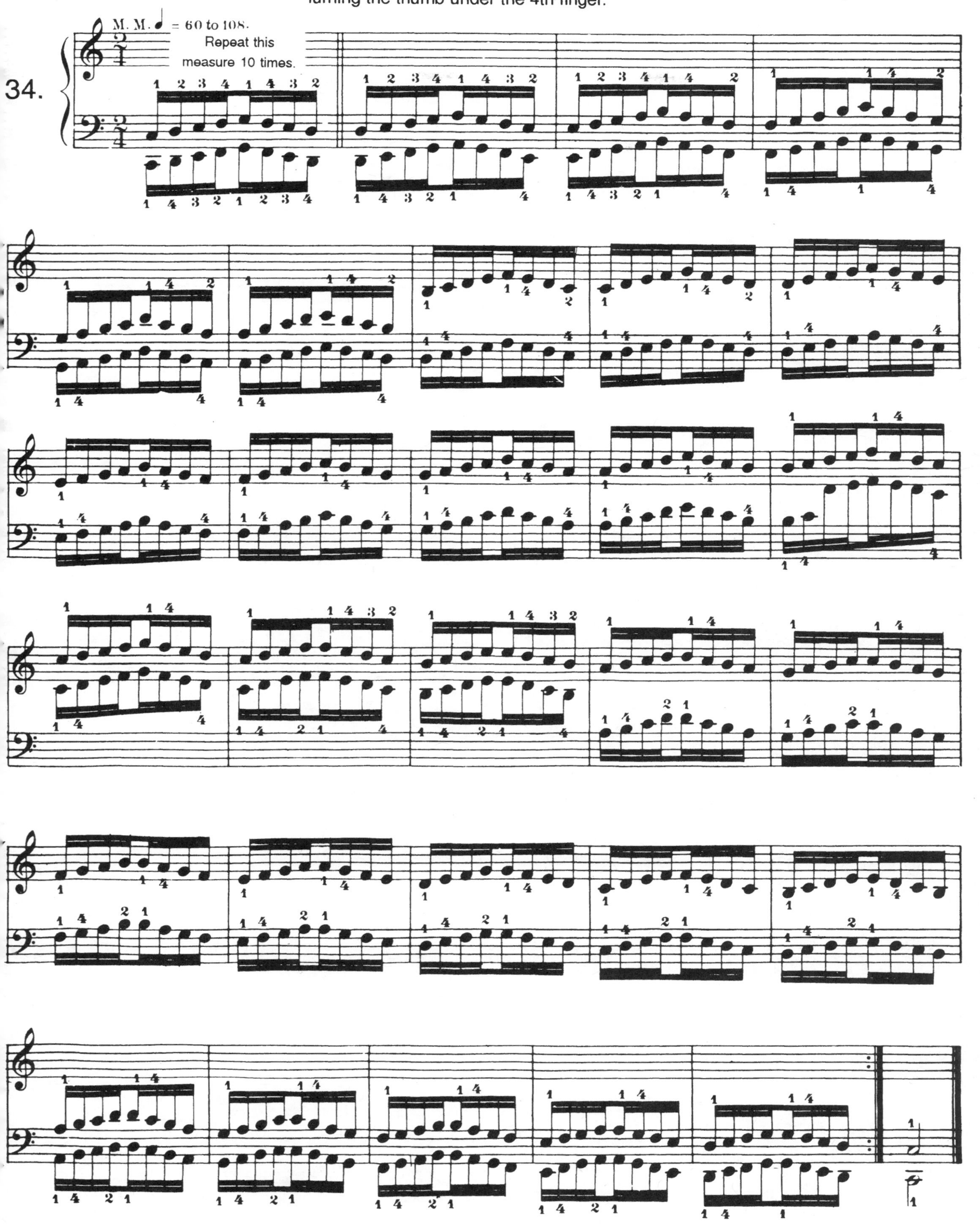

This exercise is of the greatest importance; turning the thumb under the 5th finger.

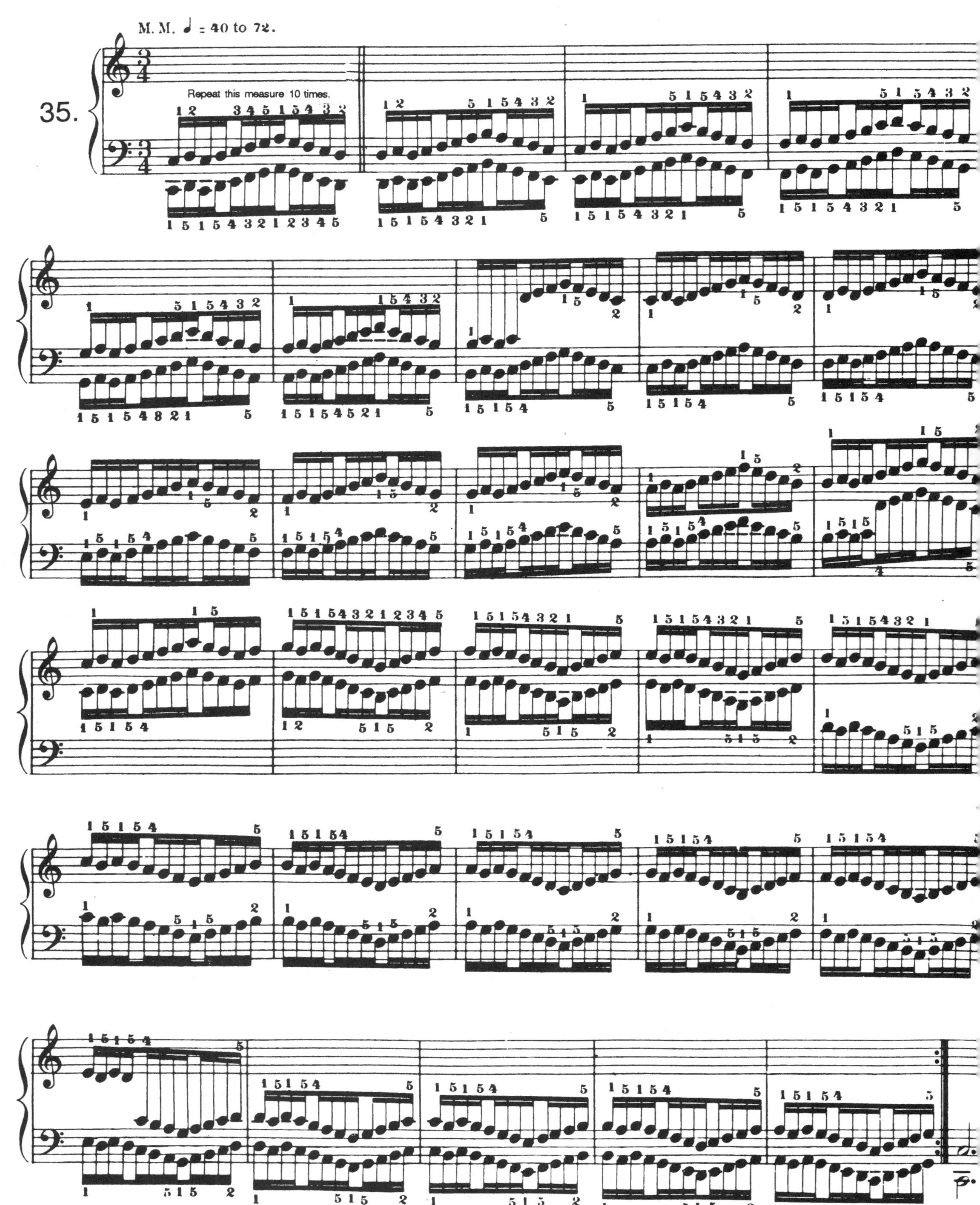

This is another exercise for turning the thumb under.

36.

This is a special exercise for turning the thumb under, played with the two thumbs only. Hold down the whole notes (A) with each hand throughout all twelve measures without striking them.

This is a preparatory scale exercise.

38.

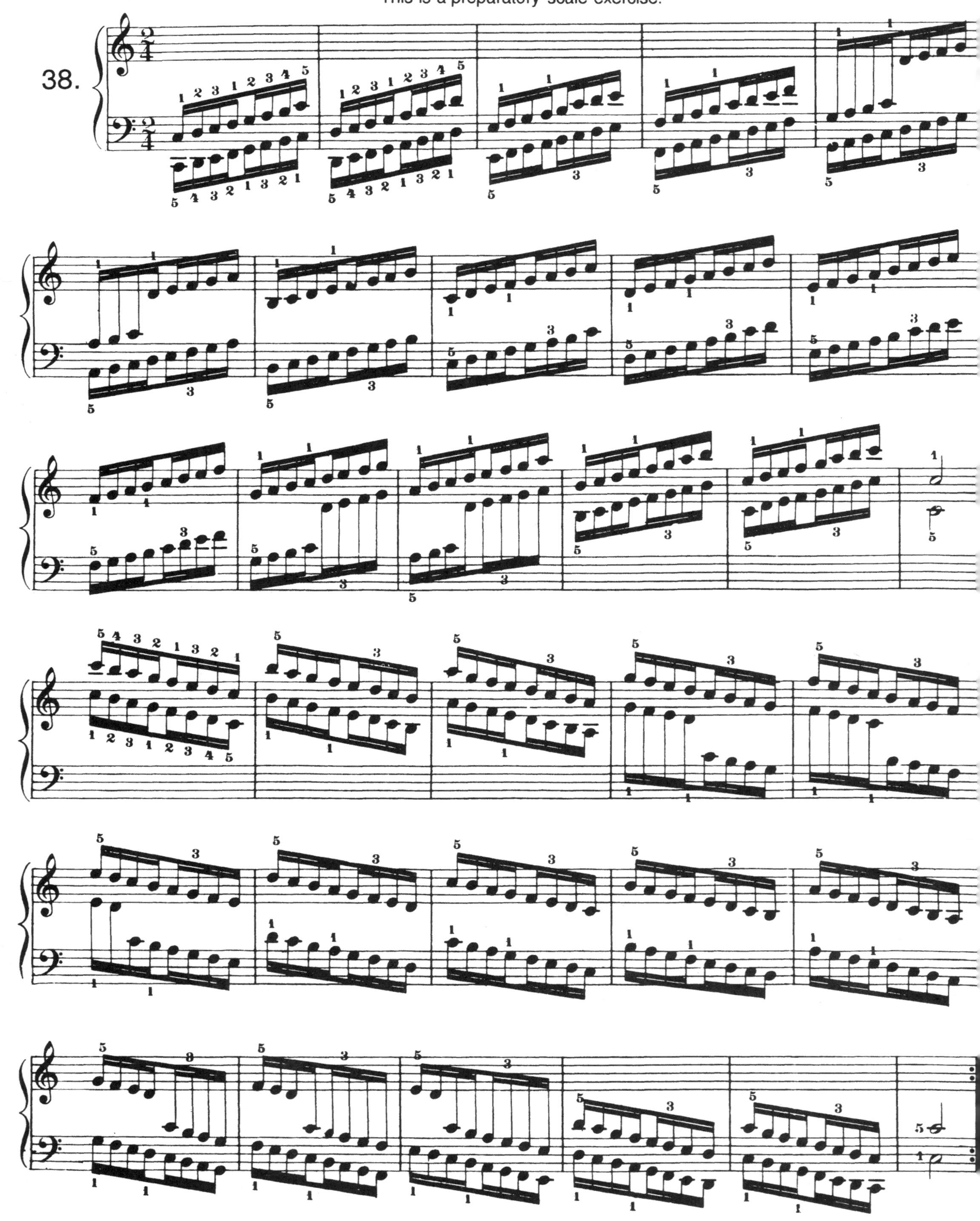

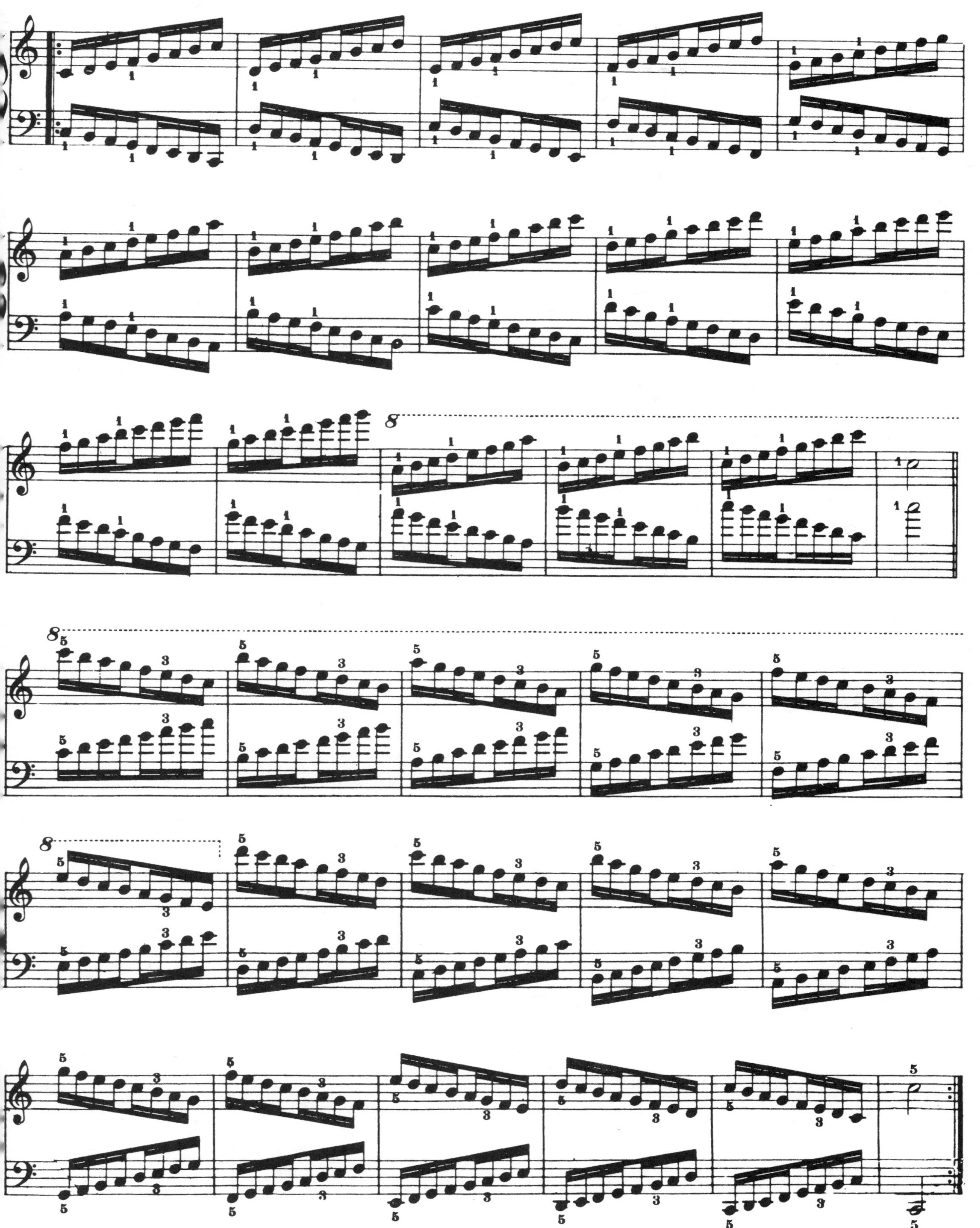

The 12 Major Scales and the 12 Minor Scales

Each major scale is followed by the two forms of it's relative minor scale. One is the HARMONIC MINOR SCALE (see 1, below) and the other is the MELODIC MINOR SCALE (see 2, below). The HARMONIC MINOR has a minor 6th, and the leading-note both ascending and descending. The MELODIC MINOR has a major 6th and the leading-note ascending, but a minor 7th and a minor 6th descending.

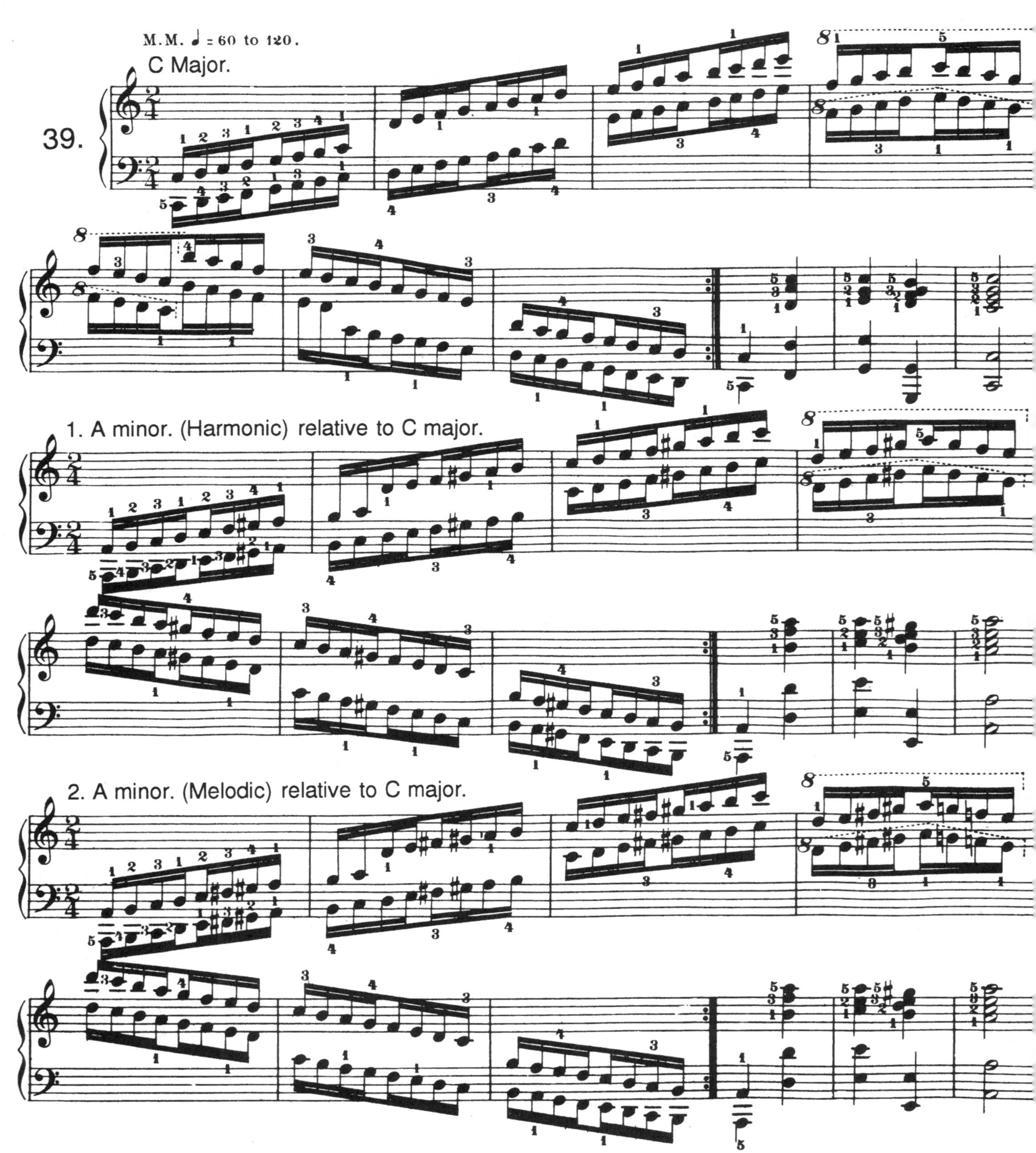

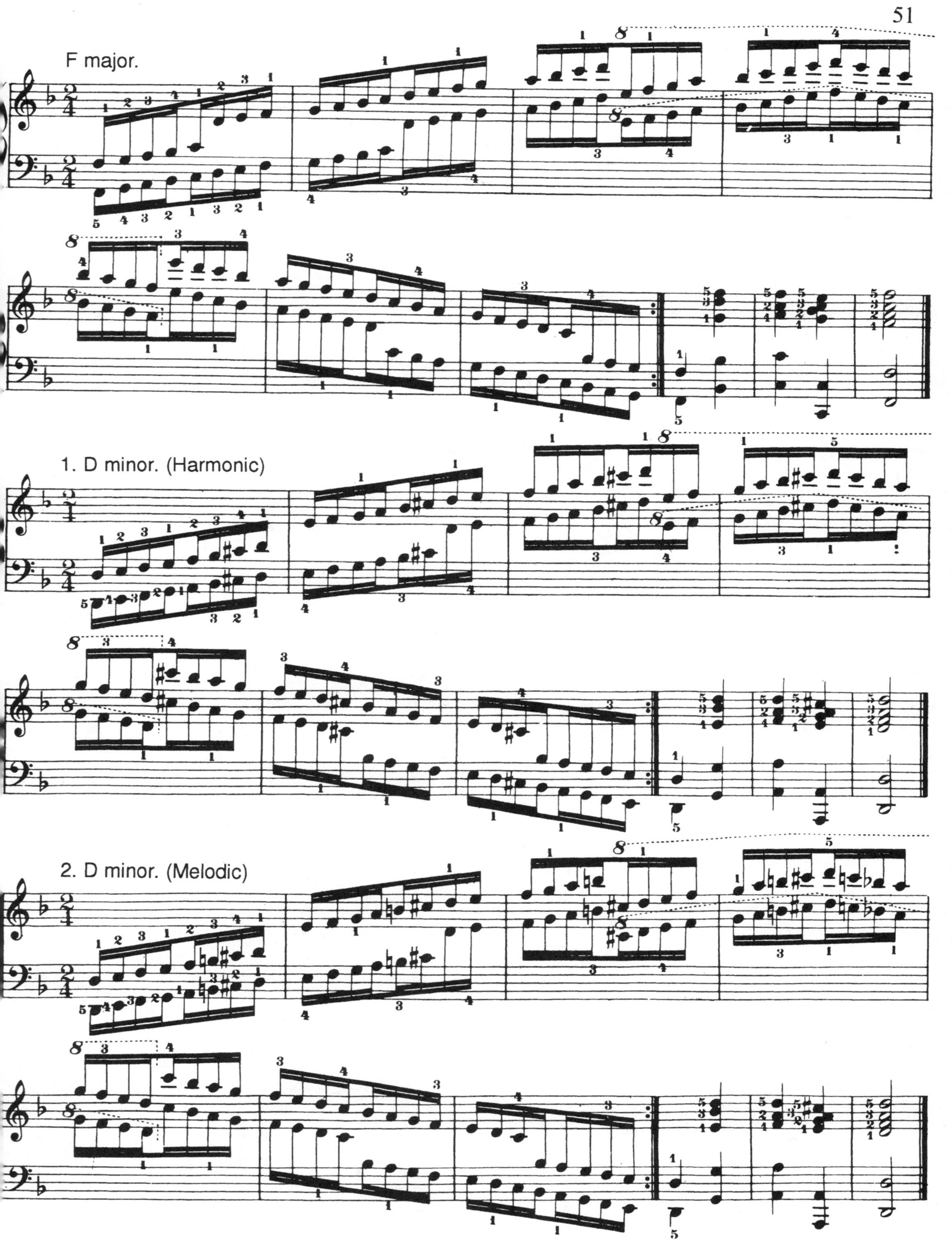
F major.
1. D minor. (Harmonic)
2. D minor. (Melodic)

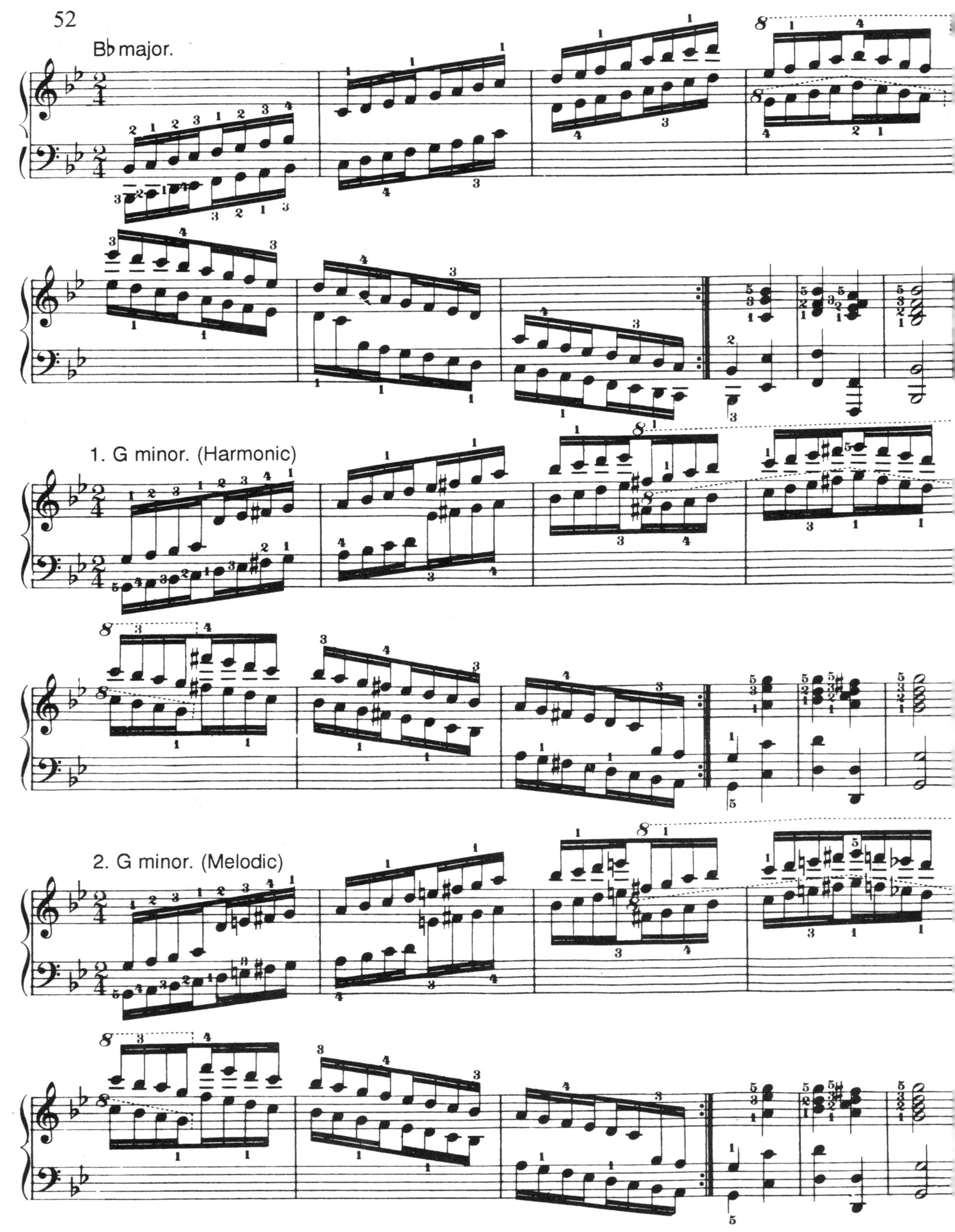
B♭ major.
1. G minor. (Harmonic)
2. G minor. (Melodic)

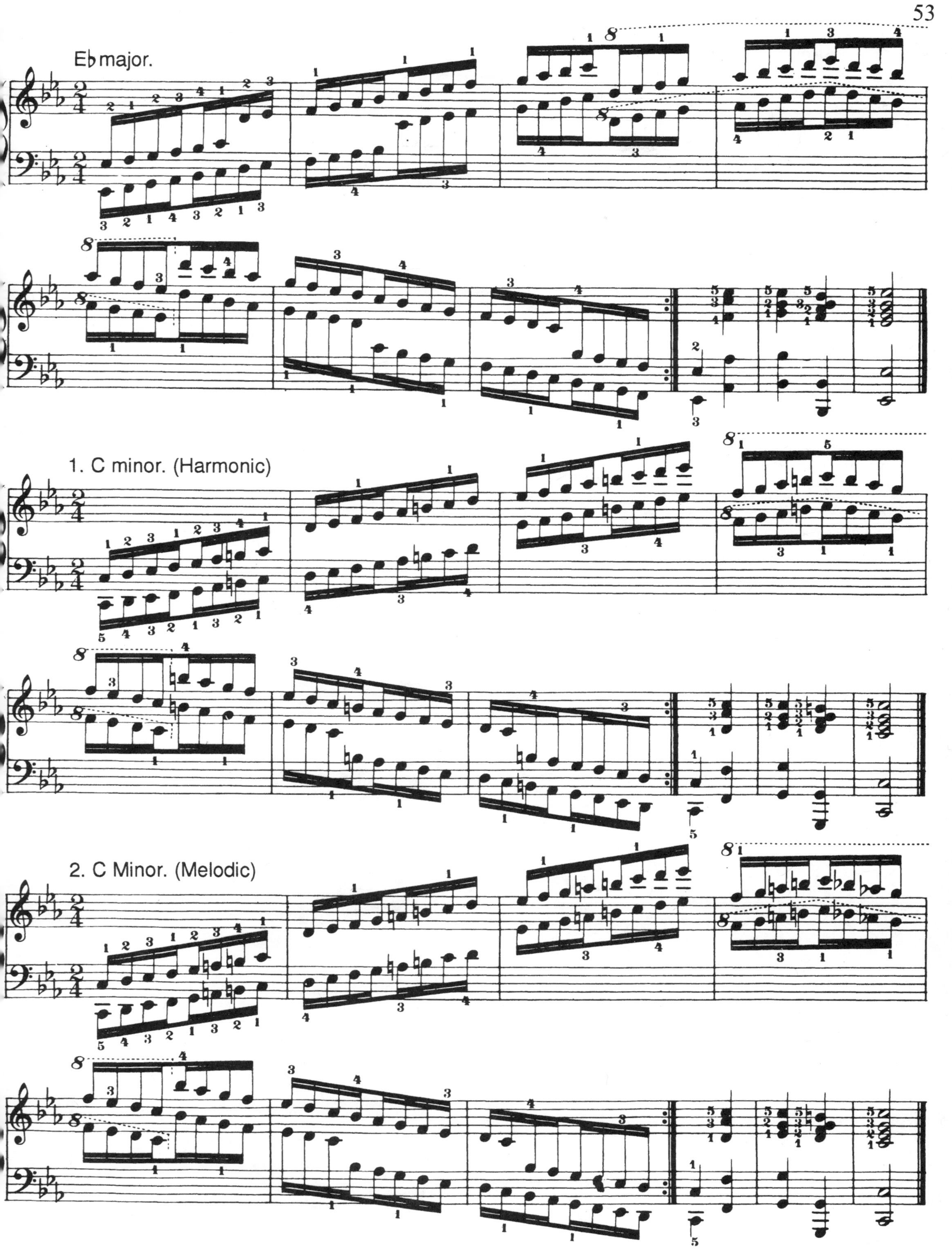
E♭ major.
1. C minor. (Harmonic)
2. C Minor. (Melodic)

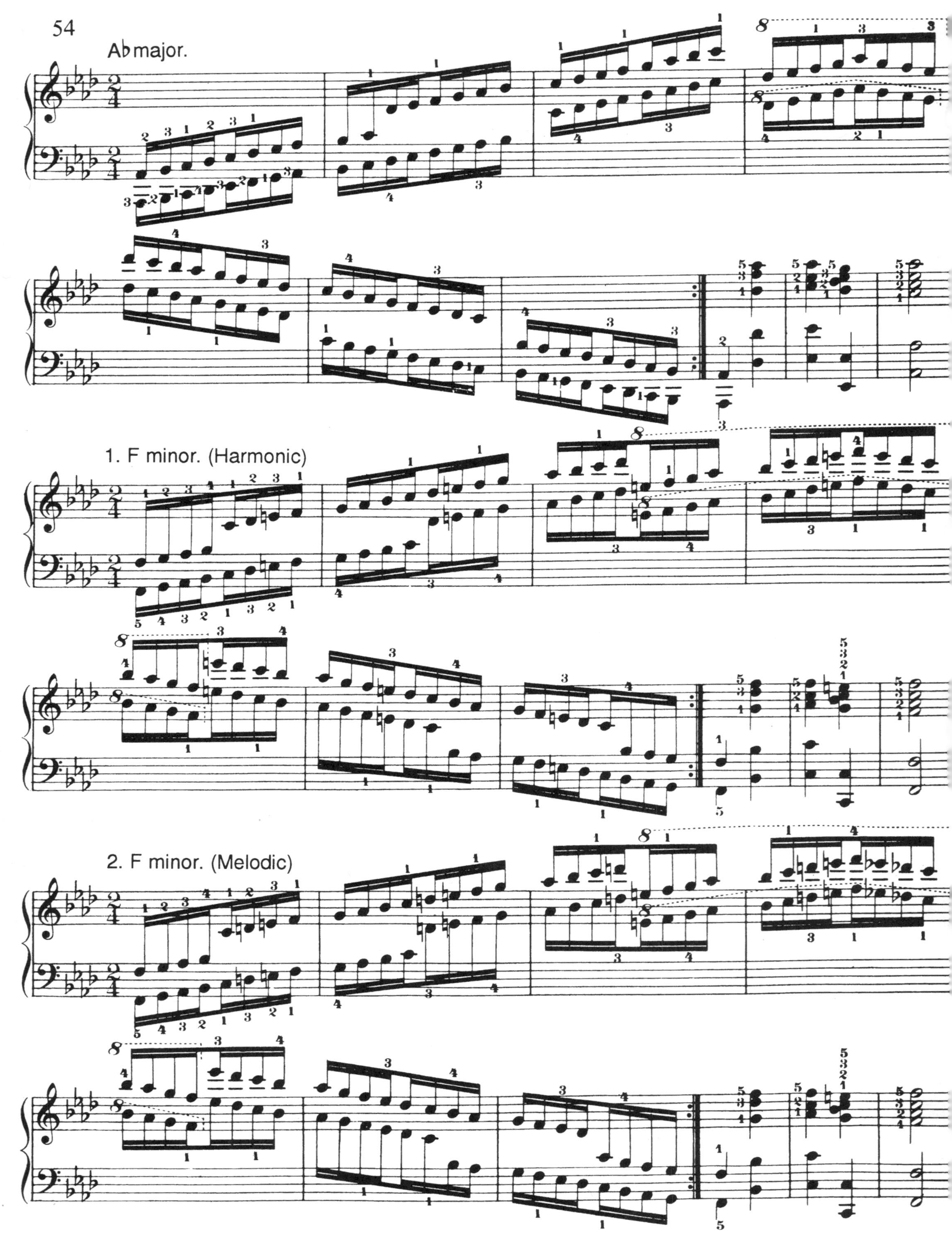
A♭ major.
1. F minor. (Harmonic)
2. F minor. (Melodic)

D♭ major.
1. B♭ minor. (Harmonic)
2. B♭ minor. (Melodic)

G♭ major.
1. E♭ minor. (Harmonic)
2. E♭ minor. (Melodic)

B major.

1. G♯ minor. (Harmonic)

2. G♯ minor. (Melodic)

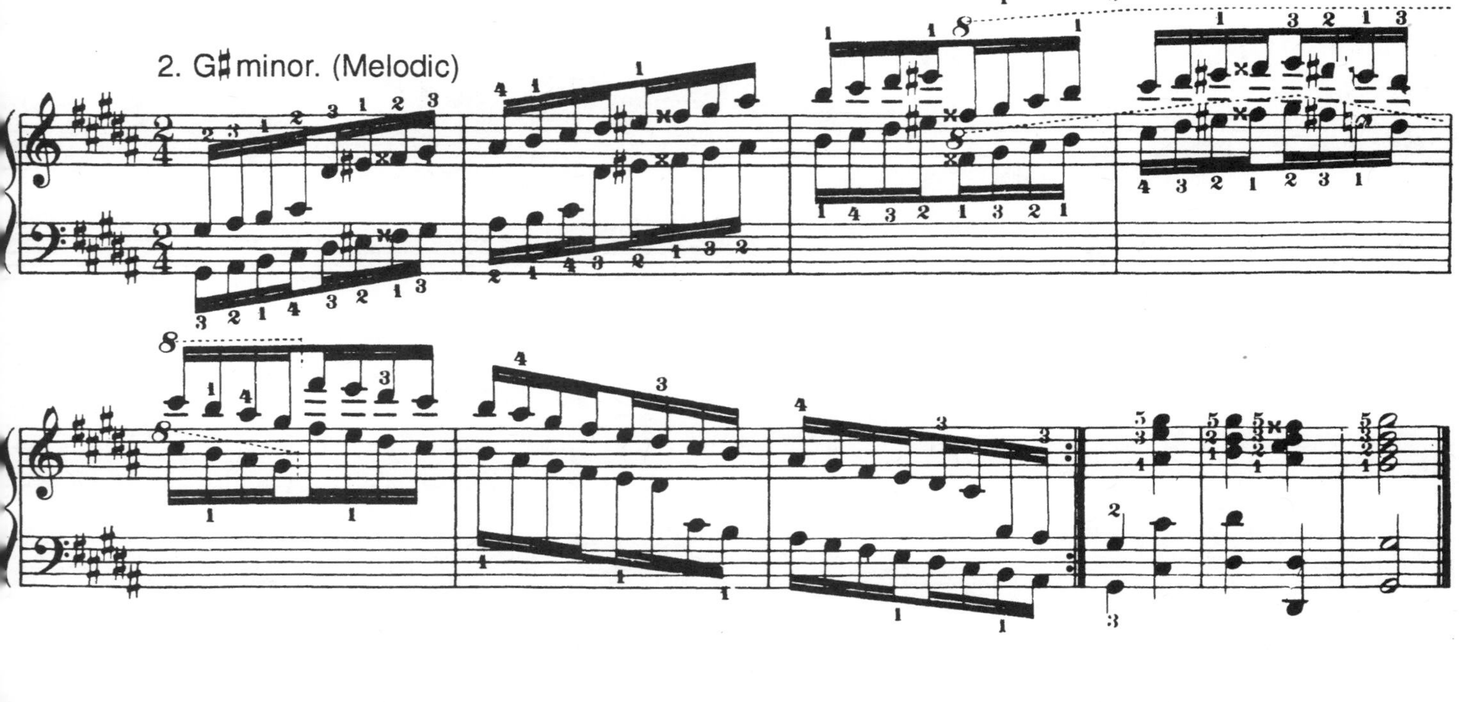

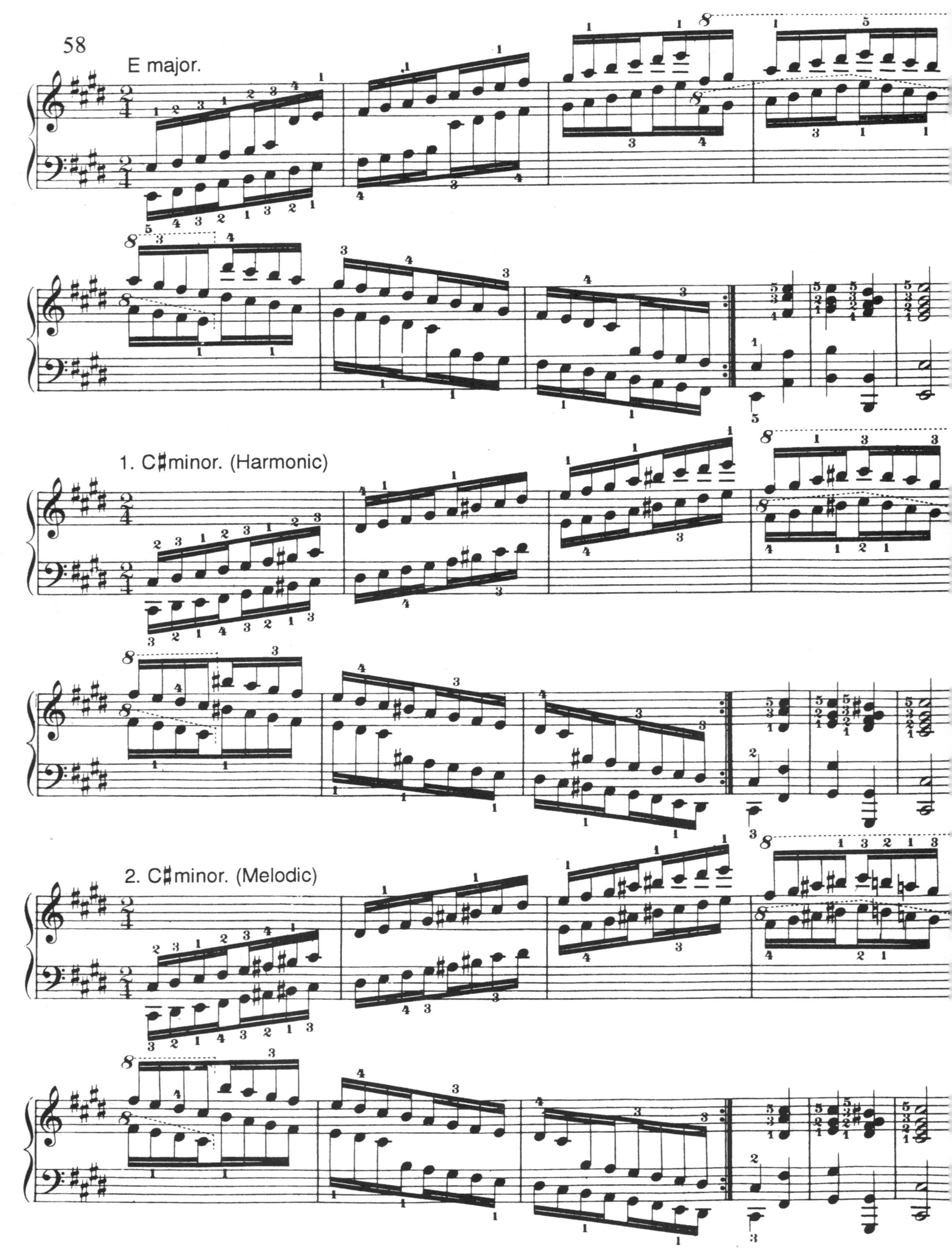
E major.
1. C♯minor. (Harmonic)
2. C♯minor. (Melodic)

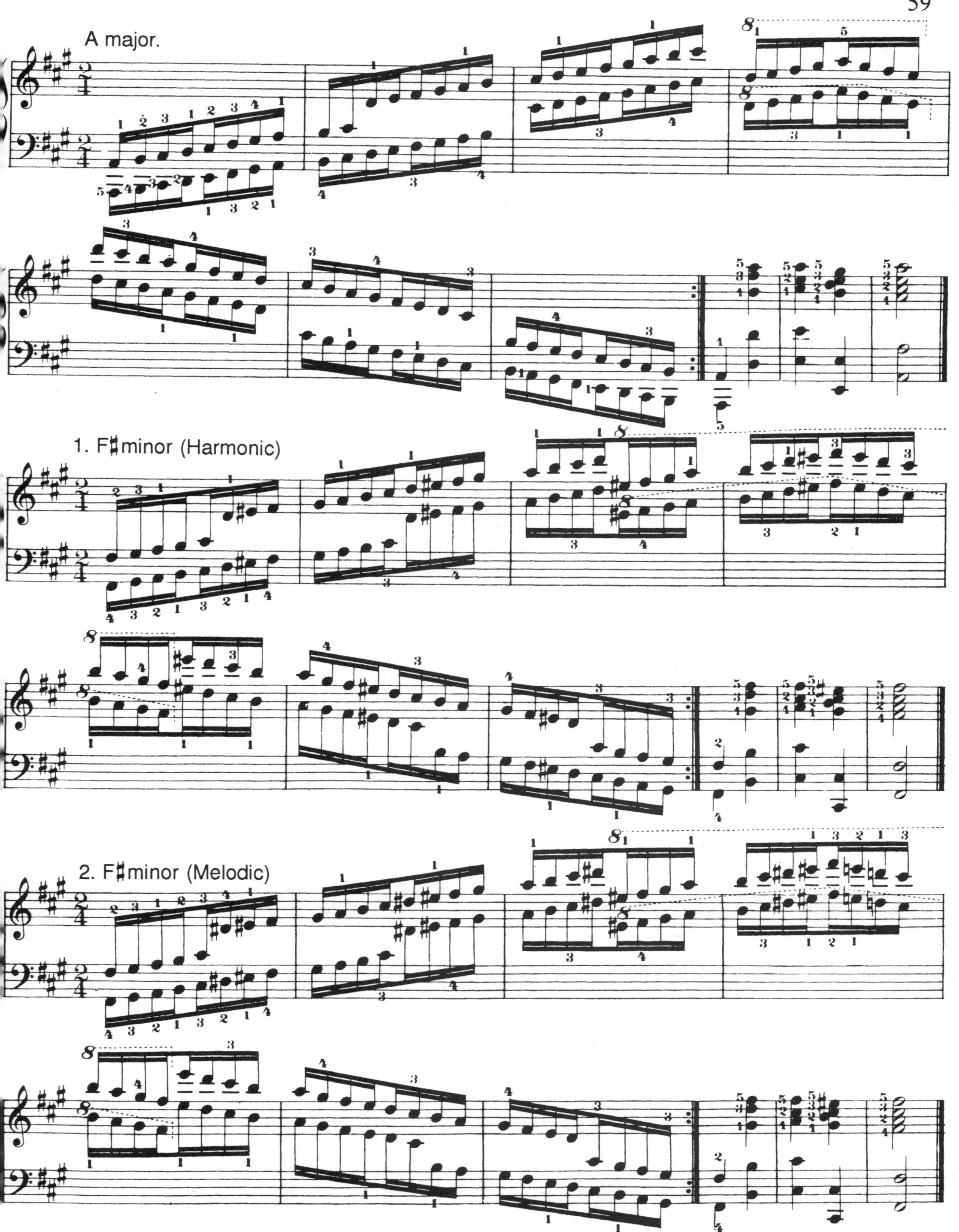
A major.
1. F♯minor (Harmonic)
2. F♯minor (Melodic)

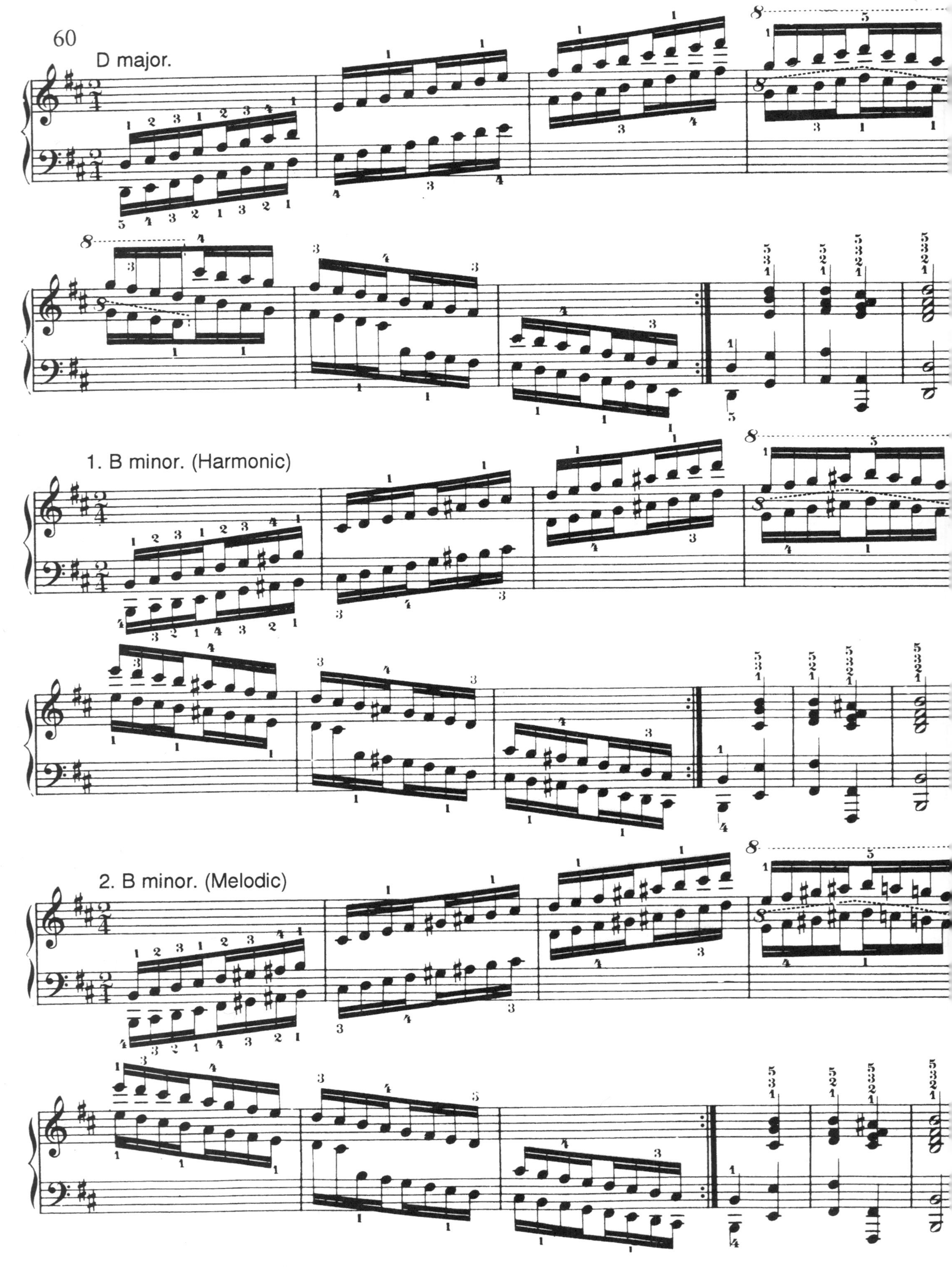
D major.
1. B minor. (Harmonic)
2. B minor. (Melodic)

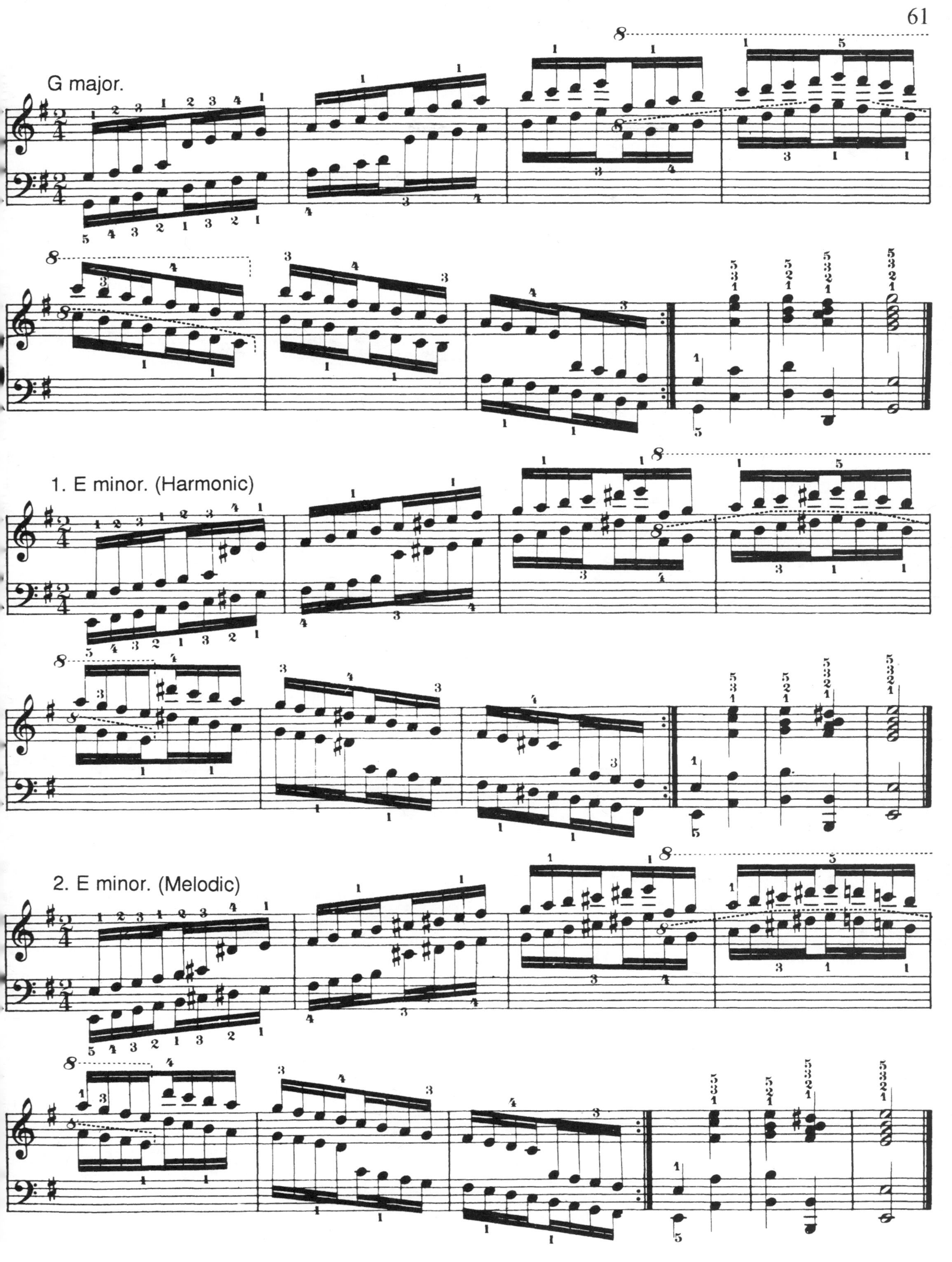
G major.
1. E minor. (Harmonic)
2. E minor. (Melodic)

Chromatic Scales

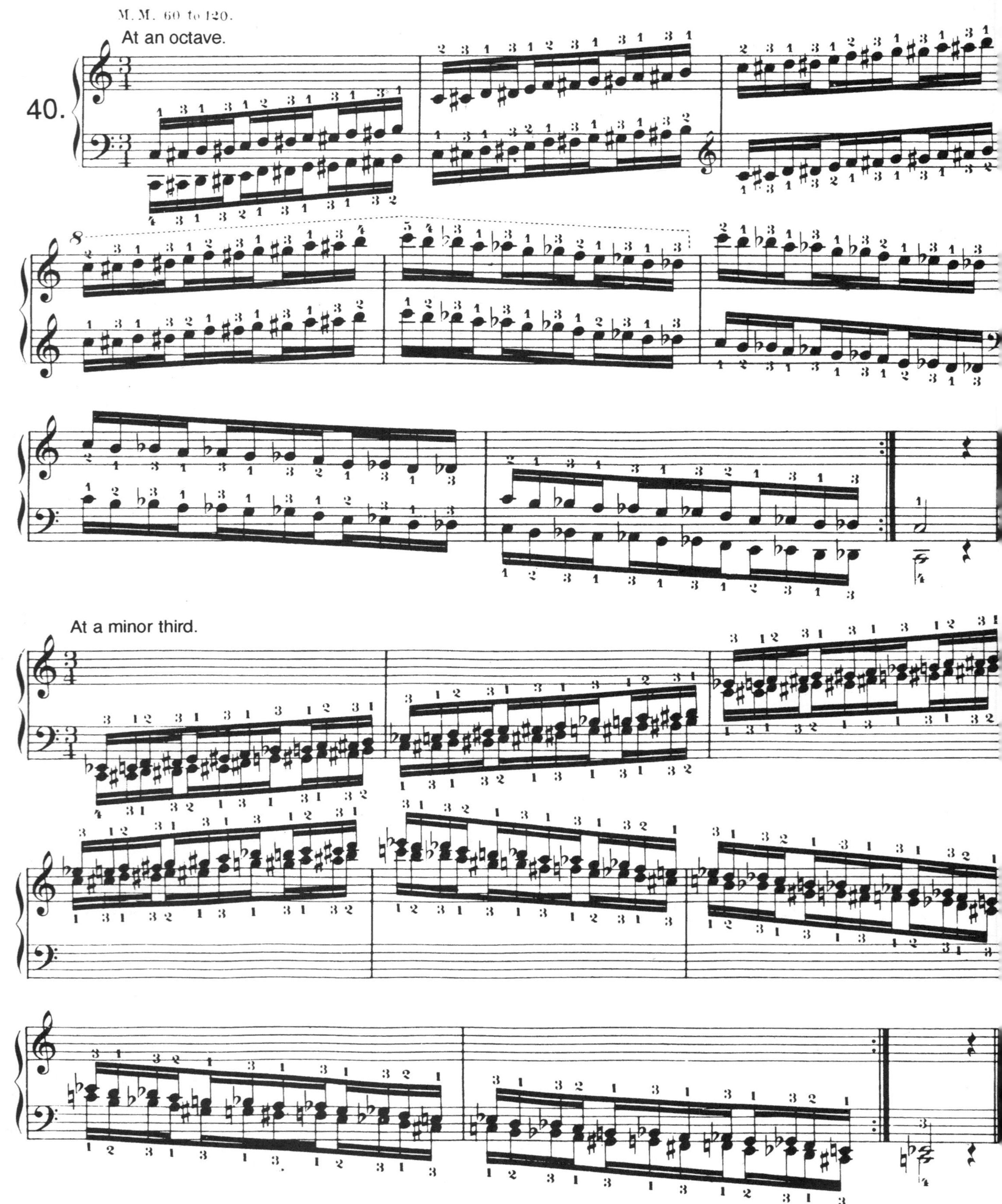

At a major sixth.

At a minor sixth.

In contrary motion, beginning on the octave.
In contrary motion, beginning on the minor third.
In contrary motion, beginning on the major third.
A fingering especially suited for legato passages.

41.
C major.
M.M. ♩= 60 to 108.
A minor,
relative to C major.
F major.
D minor.
B♭major.
G minor.

E♭ major.
C minor.
A♭ major.
F minor.
D♭ major.
B♭ minor.

G♭major.
E♭minor.
B major.
G♯minor.
E major.
C♯minor.

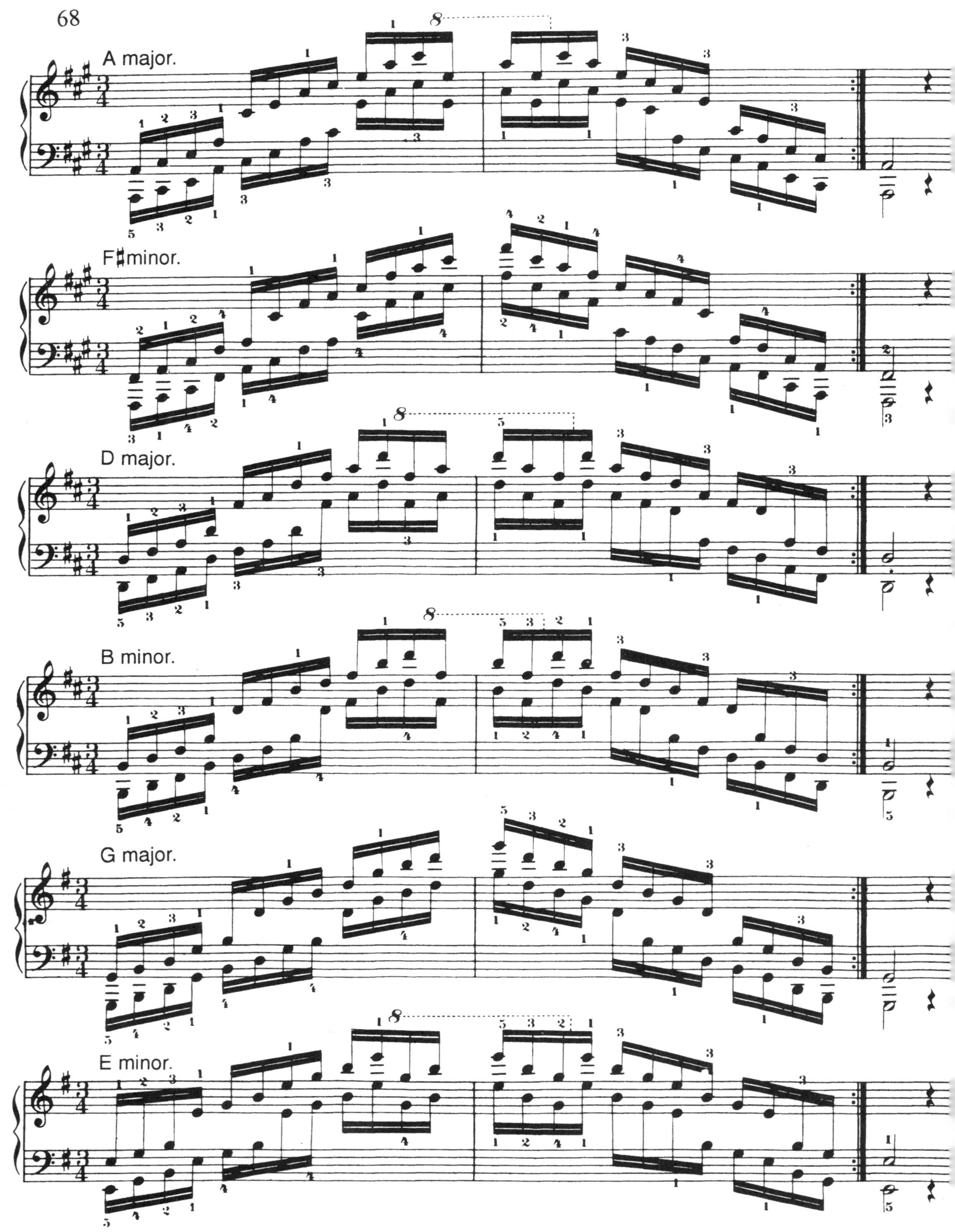
A major.
F♯minor.
D major.
B minor.
G major.
E minor.

Arpeggios on the diminished seventh chord in 7 keys.
(For extension of the fingers)

4 times.

Arpeggios on the dominant seventh chord, in 7 keys.

(For extension of the fingers)

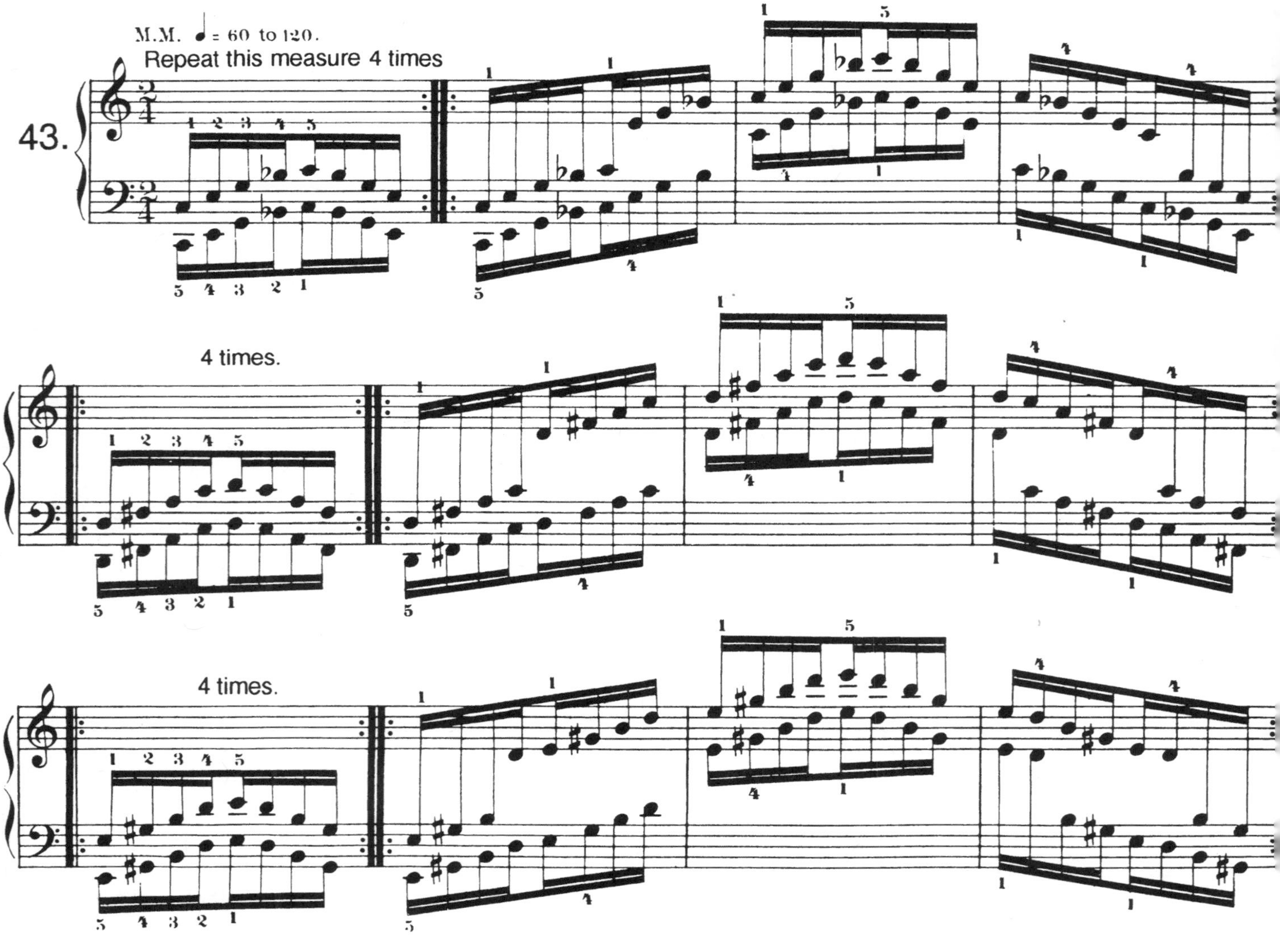

M.M. ♩ = 60 to 120.

Repeat this measure 4 times

43.

4 times.

4 times.

End of Part 2

It is recommended that parts 1 & 2 be mastered before proceeding to part 3.

The Virtuoso Pianist Part 3.

Virtuoso Exercises for Mastering the Greatest Technical Difficulties.

Repeated notes in groups of three.

Fingers should be lifted high and with precision, without moving the hand or wrist. Practice the first four measures until mastered, then proceed with the rest of the exercise.

C. L. Hanon

44.

simile

Repeated Notes In Groups Of Two For All Five Fingers.

Each fingering should be mastered before proceeding to the next. When completed, play the entire exercise without stopping.

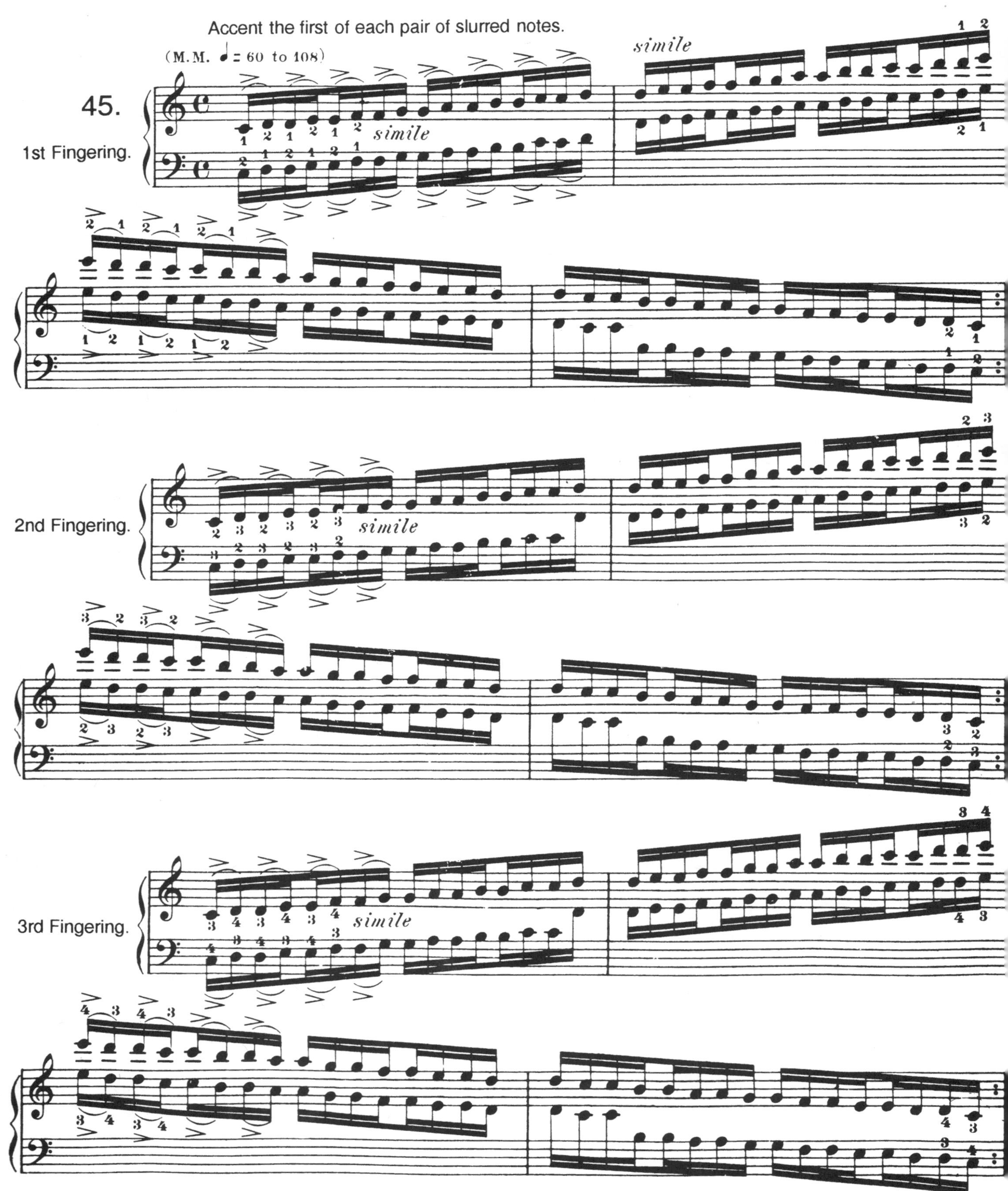

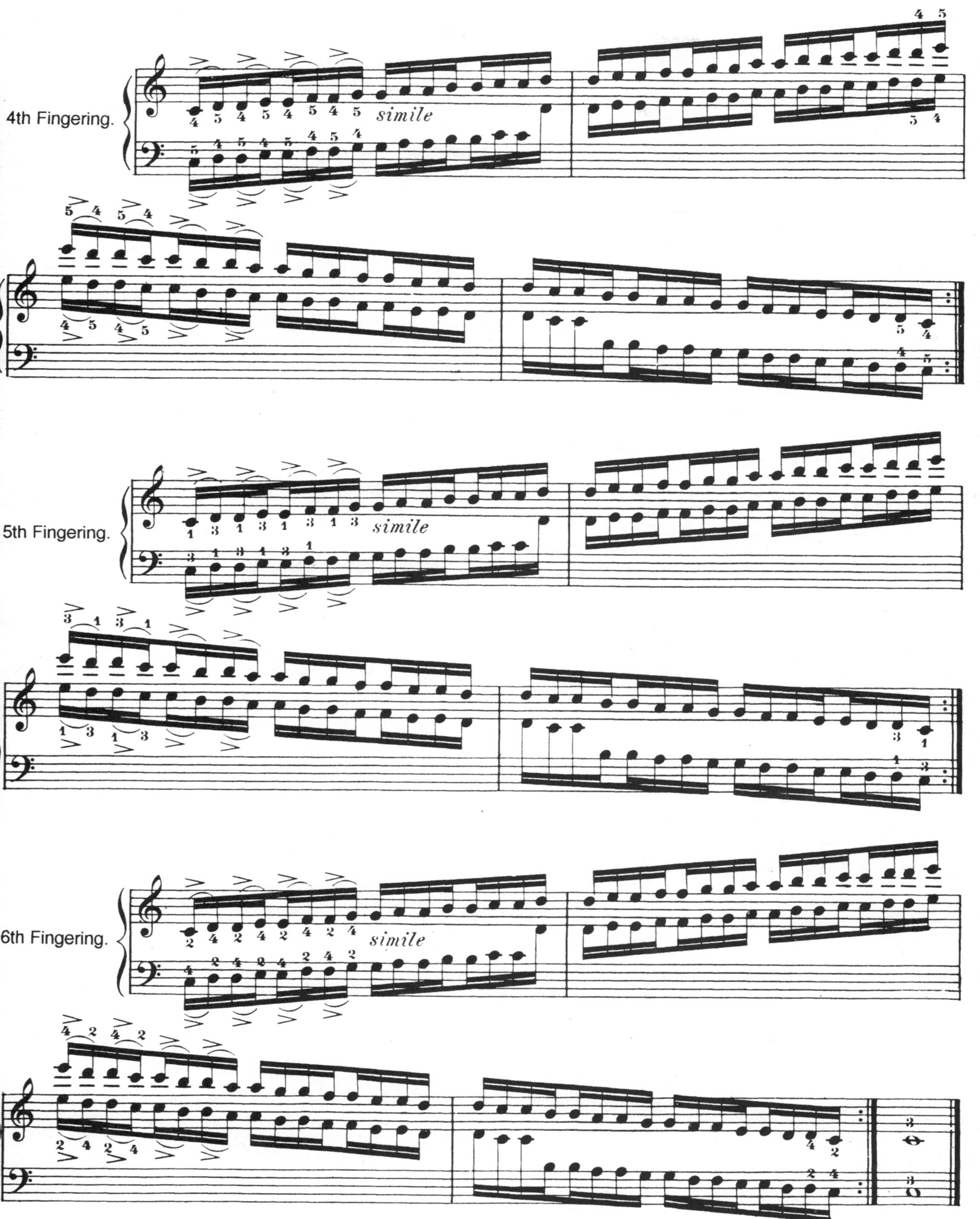
4th Fingering.
simile
5th Fingering.
simile
6th Fingering.
simile

The Trill

For All Five Fingers.

Practice the first 6 measures until they can be played at quite a rapid tempo before continuing through the exercise. When the fingering changes (A) it is extremely important to make the change with absolute evenness.

Mozart used this exercise for the study of the trill.
Thalberg's trill.

Repeated Notes In Groups Of Four.

Fingers should be lifted high and with precision, without moving the hand or wrist. Practice the first four measures until they are mastered, then proceed with the rest of the exercise.

Wrist Exercise.

Wrist-exercise on detached thirds and wrist-exercise on detached sixths.

Lift the wrist high after each stroke keeping the arms still, the wrists flexible, and the fingers firm, but not rigid. Practice the first four measures until mastered, then proceed with the rest of the exercise.

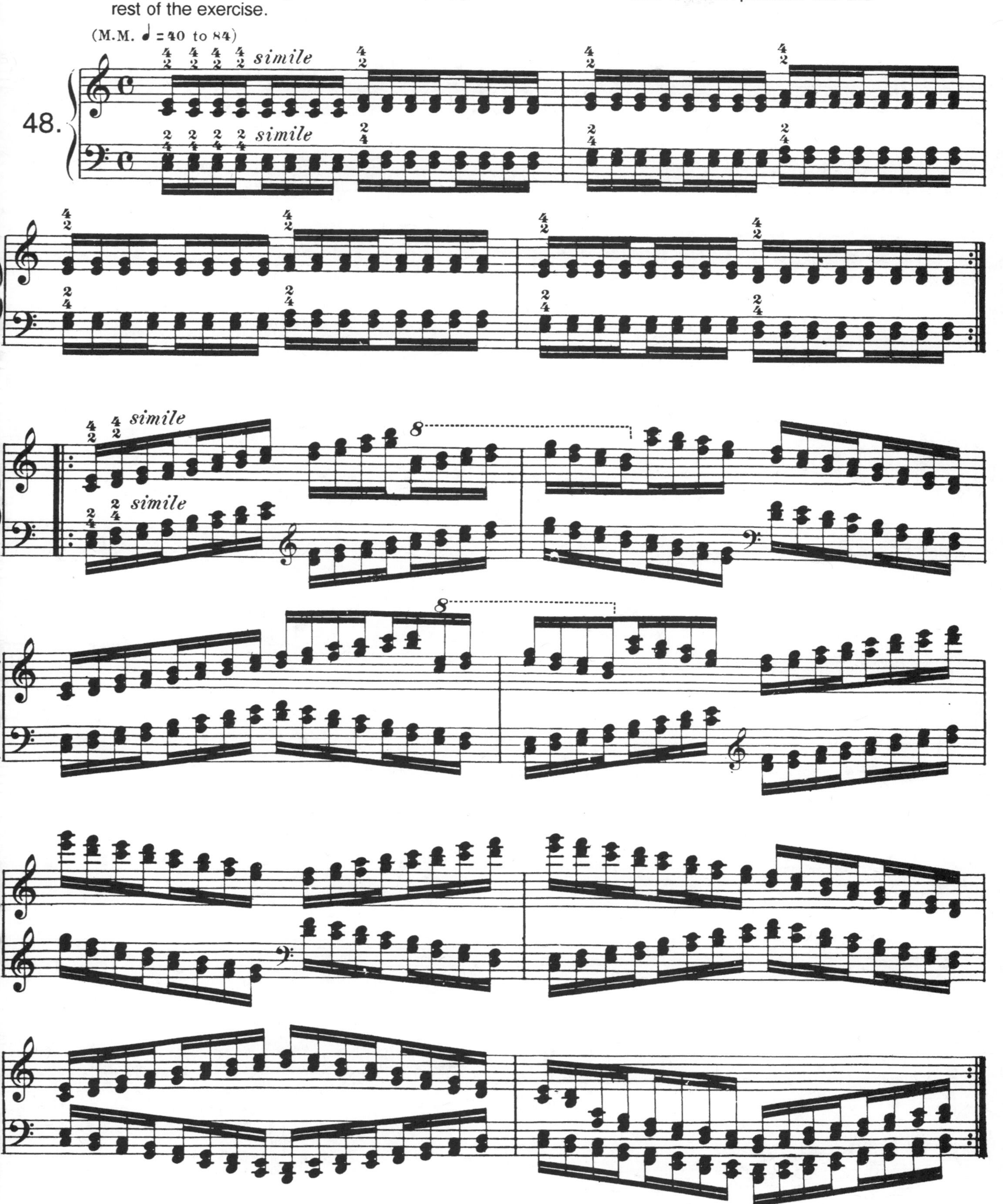

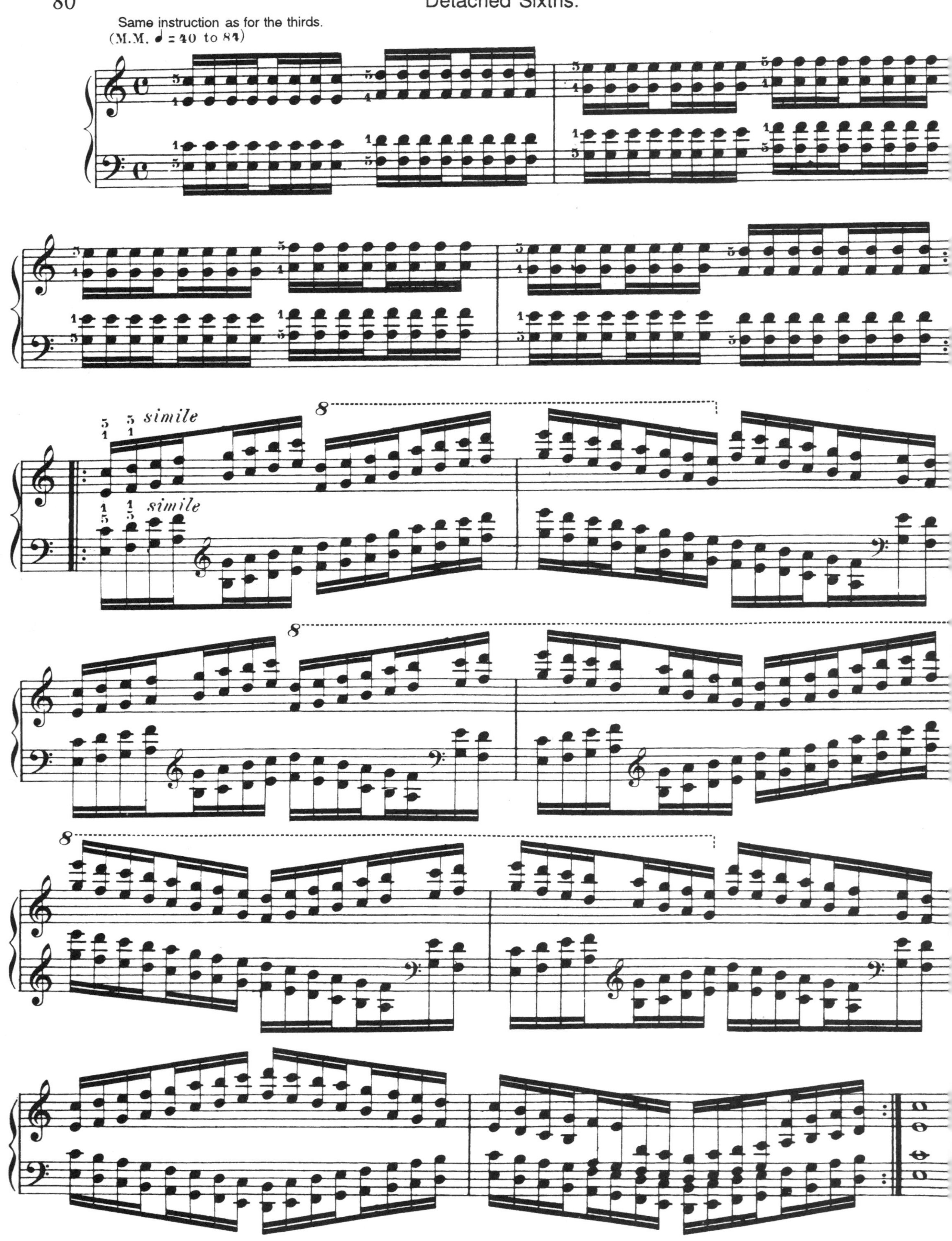
Same instruction as for the thirds.
(M.M. ♩ = 40 to 84)
simile
simile

No. 49

This exercise is for the stretch between 1st and 4th fingers, and the 2nd and 5th fingers of both hands.

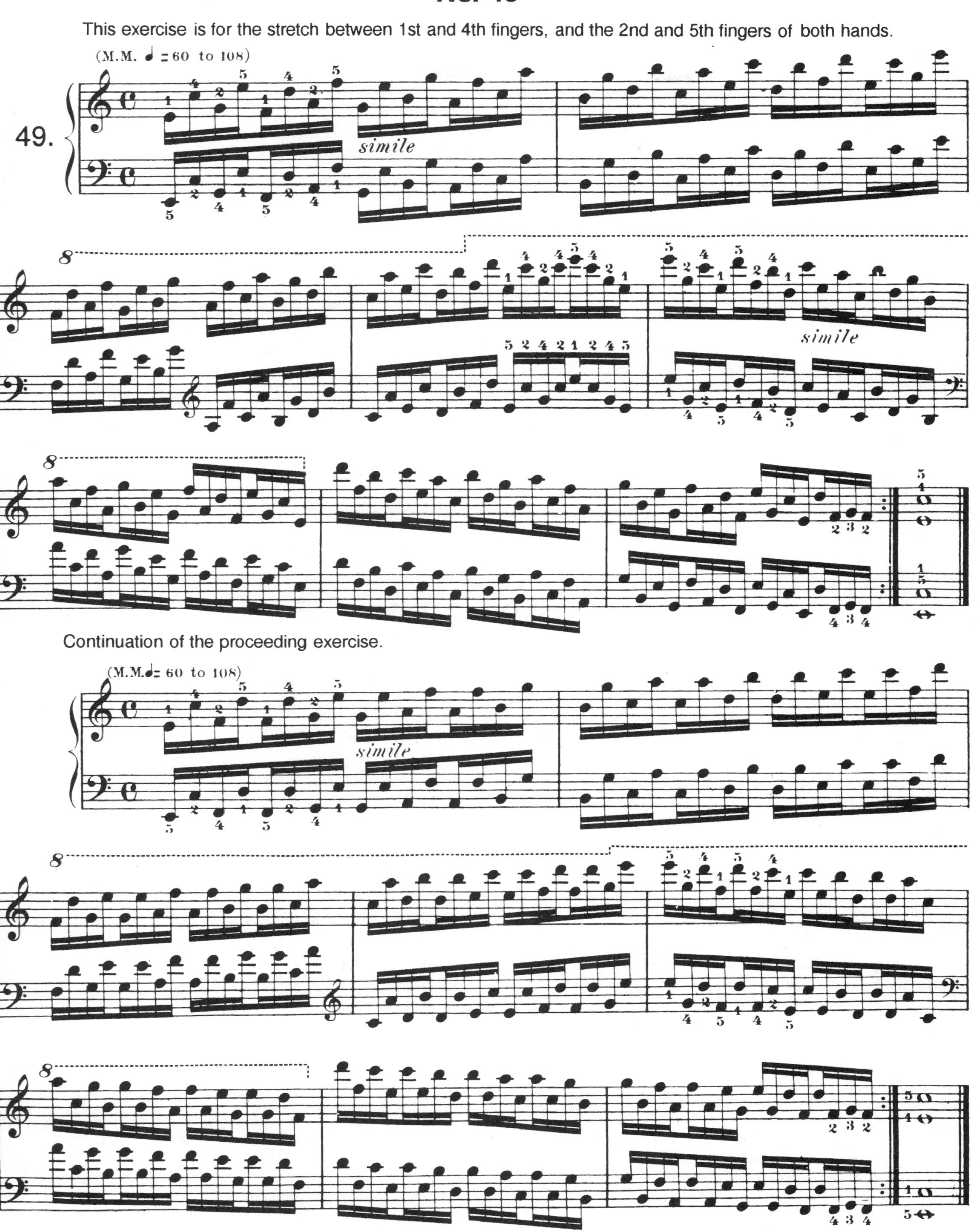

Legato Thirds.

As thirds are used so frequently in difficult music, we recommend a careful study of this exercise. All notes must be struck distinctly and evenly.

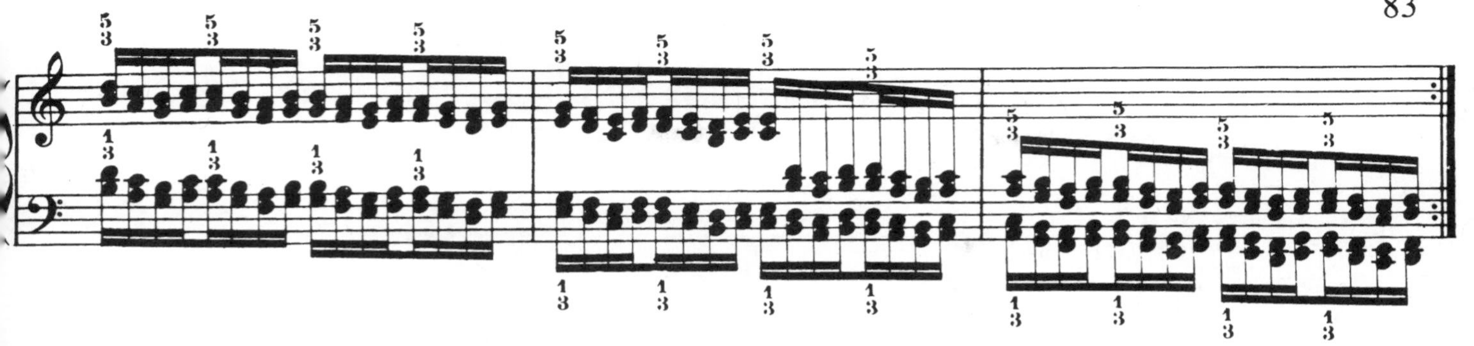

Scales In Legato Thirds.

The studies in legato thirds is also most important. To achieve a smooth legato, keep the 5th finger of the right hand on it's note while the thumb and 3rd finger pass over to the next third. Similarly, on the left hand, the thumb should be held slightly. Half notes indicate notes to be held (A). Proceed similarly in the chromatic scale further on, and in all scales in thirds.

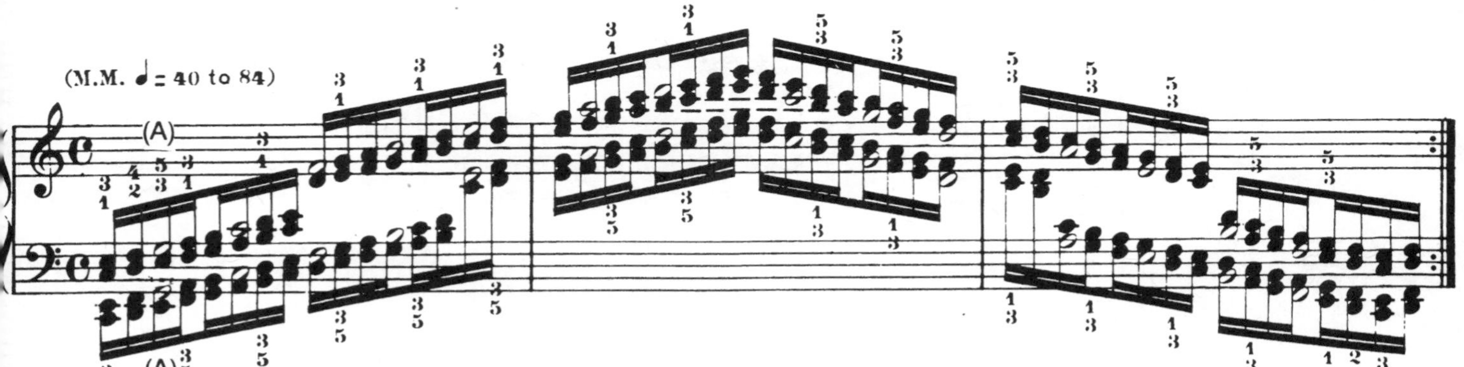

(M.M. ♩= 40 to 84)

(A)

(A)

Chromatic Scales in Minor Thirds.

(M.M. ♩= 40 to 84)

Preparatory Exercise For Scales In Octaves.

Keep the wrist flexible, the fingers playing the octaves firm, but not rigid, and the fingers not playing in a slightly rounded position. Repeat the first 8 measures slowly until a good wrist movement is achieved, then gradually accelerating to complete the exercise. If the wrists become tired, decrease the speed and then gradually increase the tempo again.

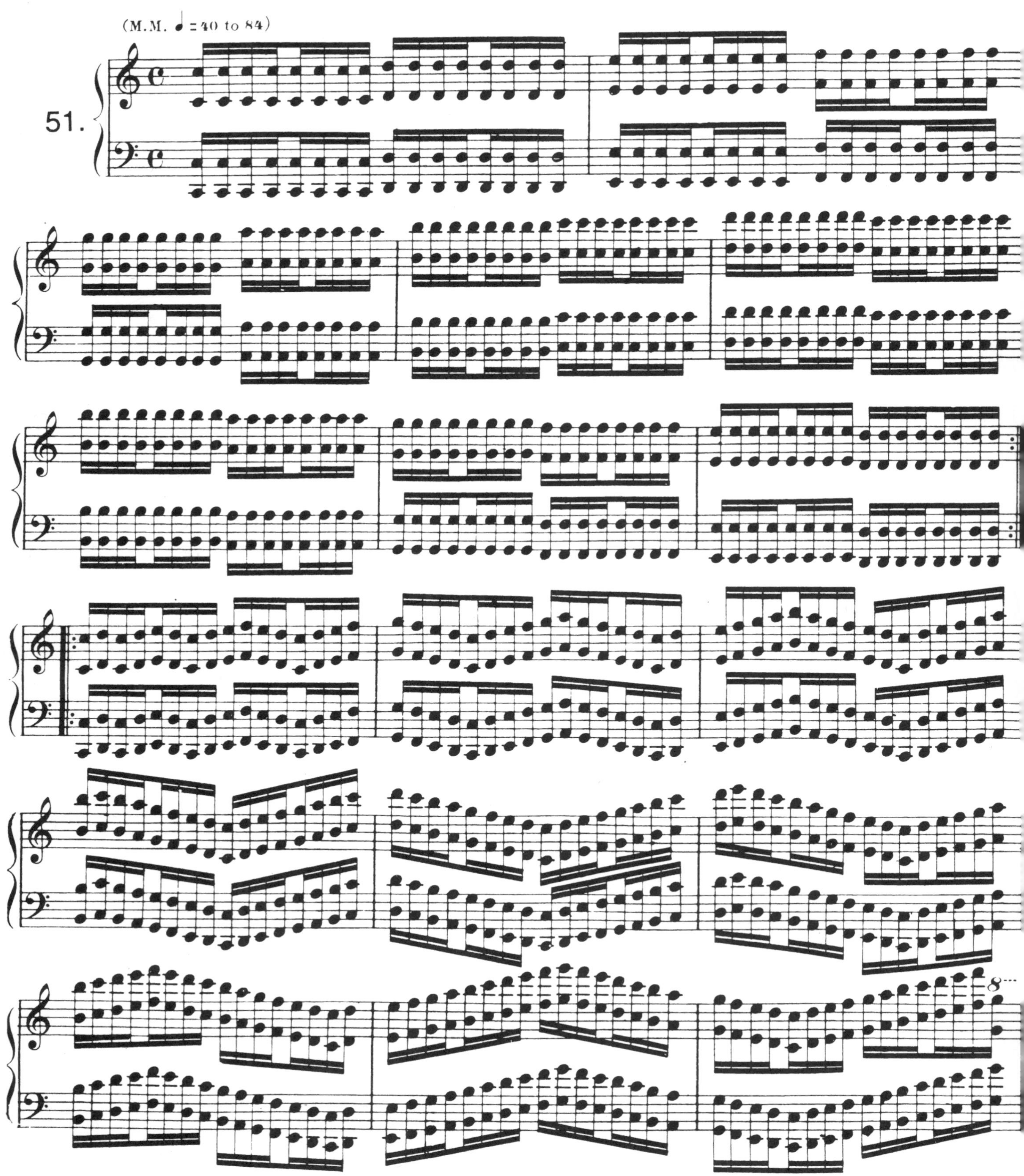

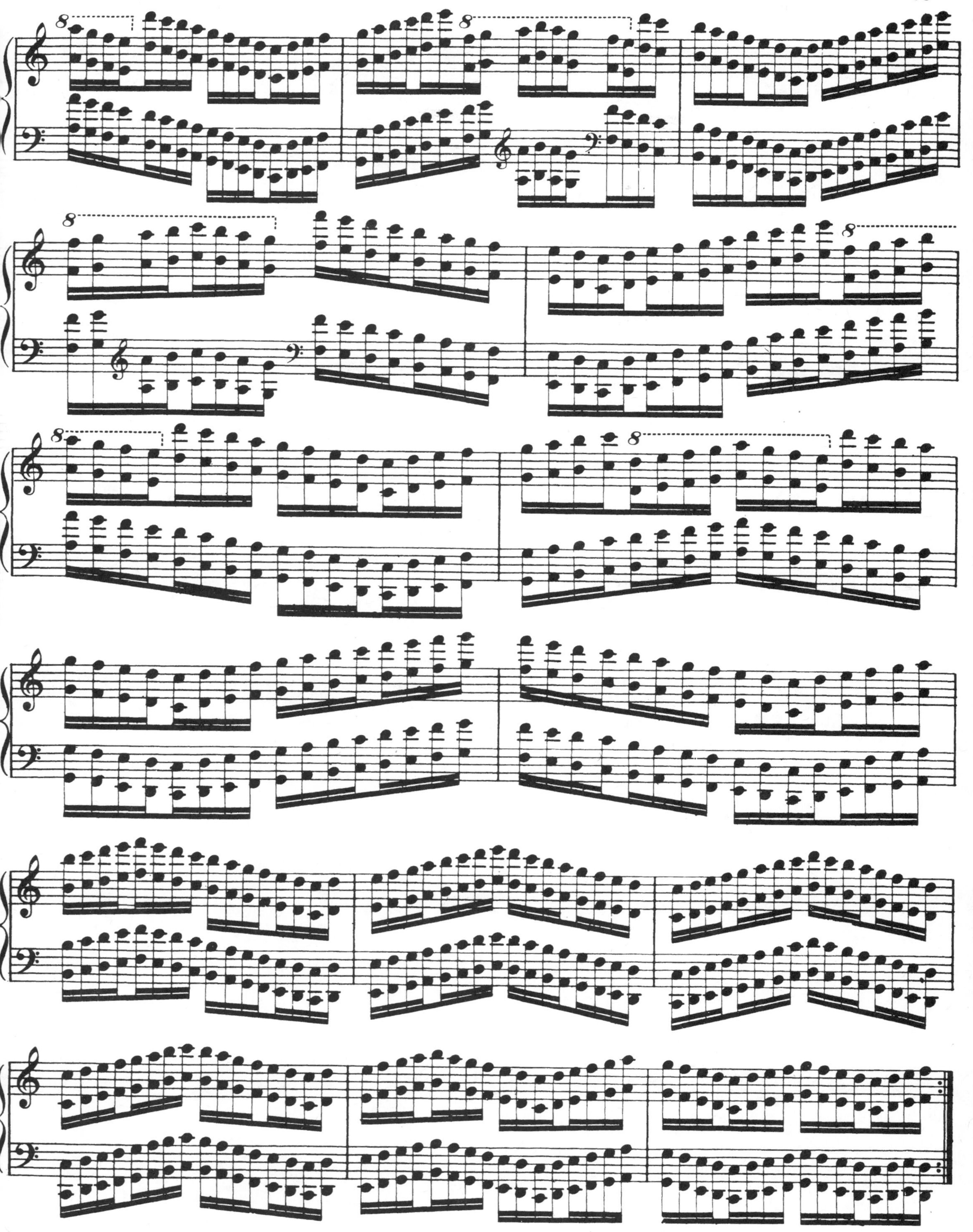
8
8
8
8
8
8

Scales in Thirds, in the Most Used Keys.

Play all scales legato and evenly. It is important to master them thoroughly. See notes to Exercise No. 50.

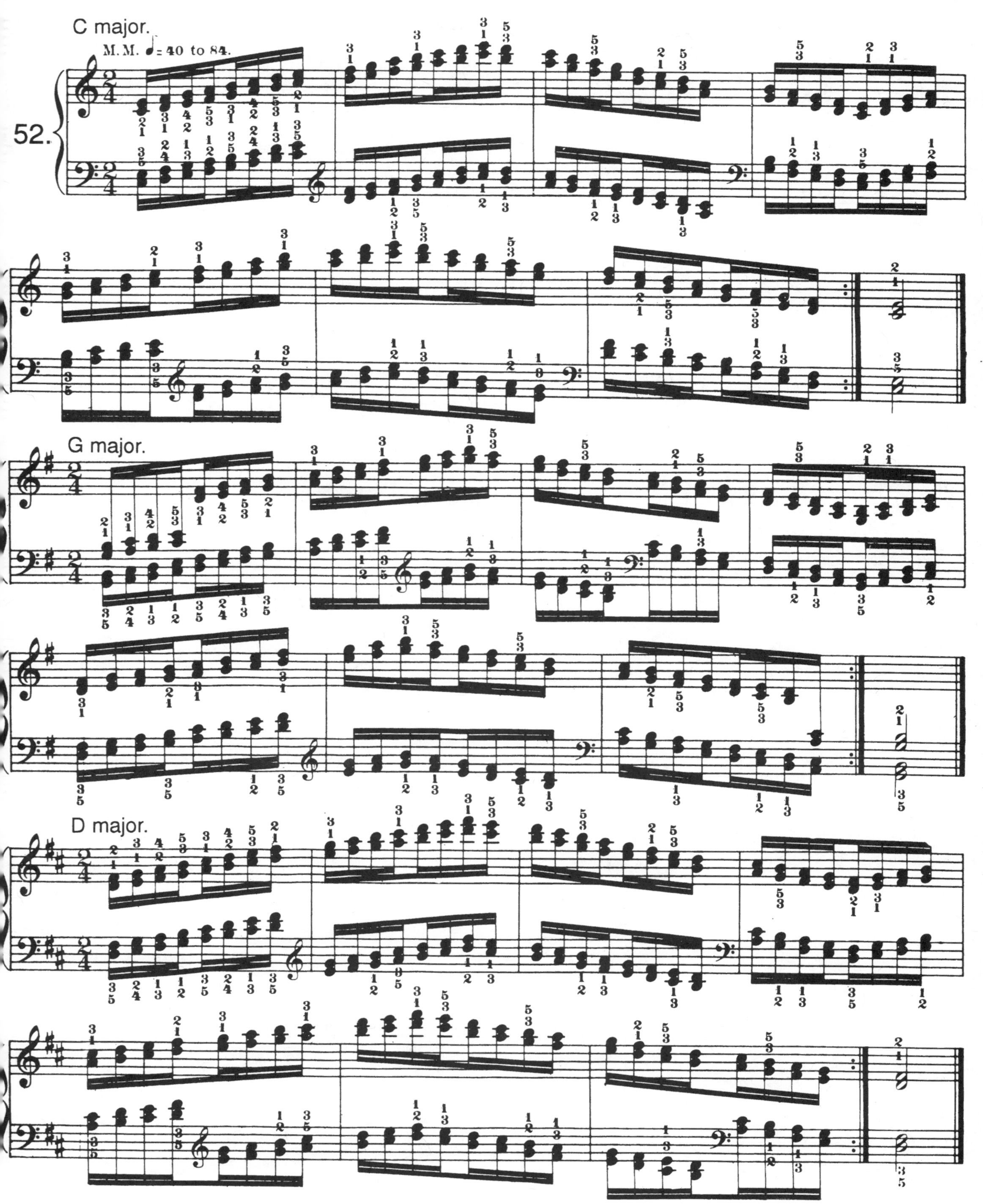

A major.
E major.
F major.

B♭ major.
E♭ major.
A♭ major.

A minor.
D minor.
G minor.

Scales In Octaves In The 24 Keys.

Practice each of the scales until they can be played easily, then play all 24 without stopping. Maintain proper wrist movement, which is the only way of ensuring that octaves are played rapidly and with vigor. In all octave scales, the black keys should be played with the fourth finger of either hand. See notes to Exercises 48 and 51.

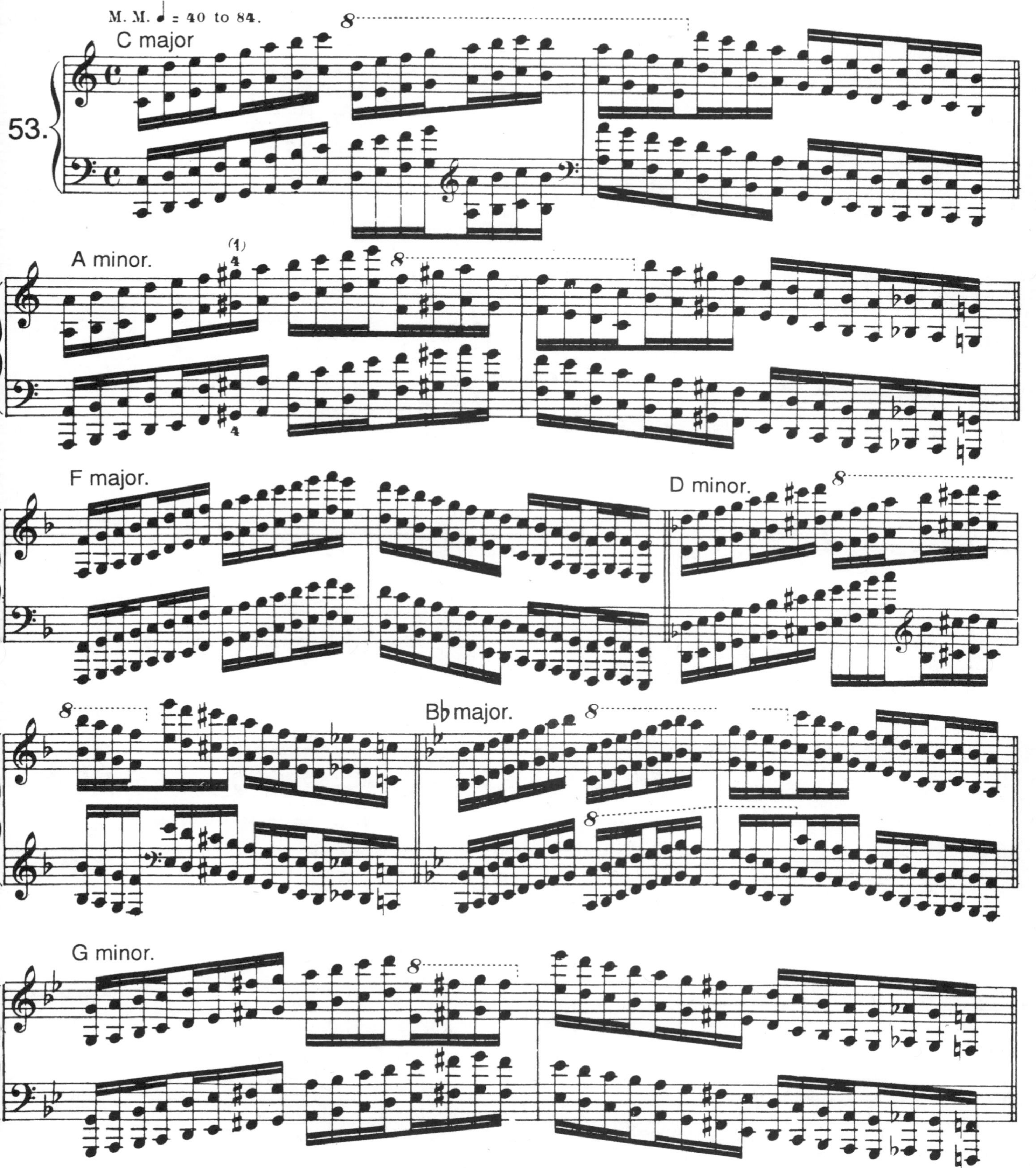

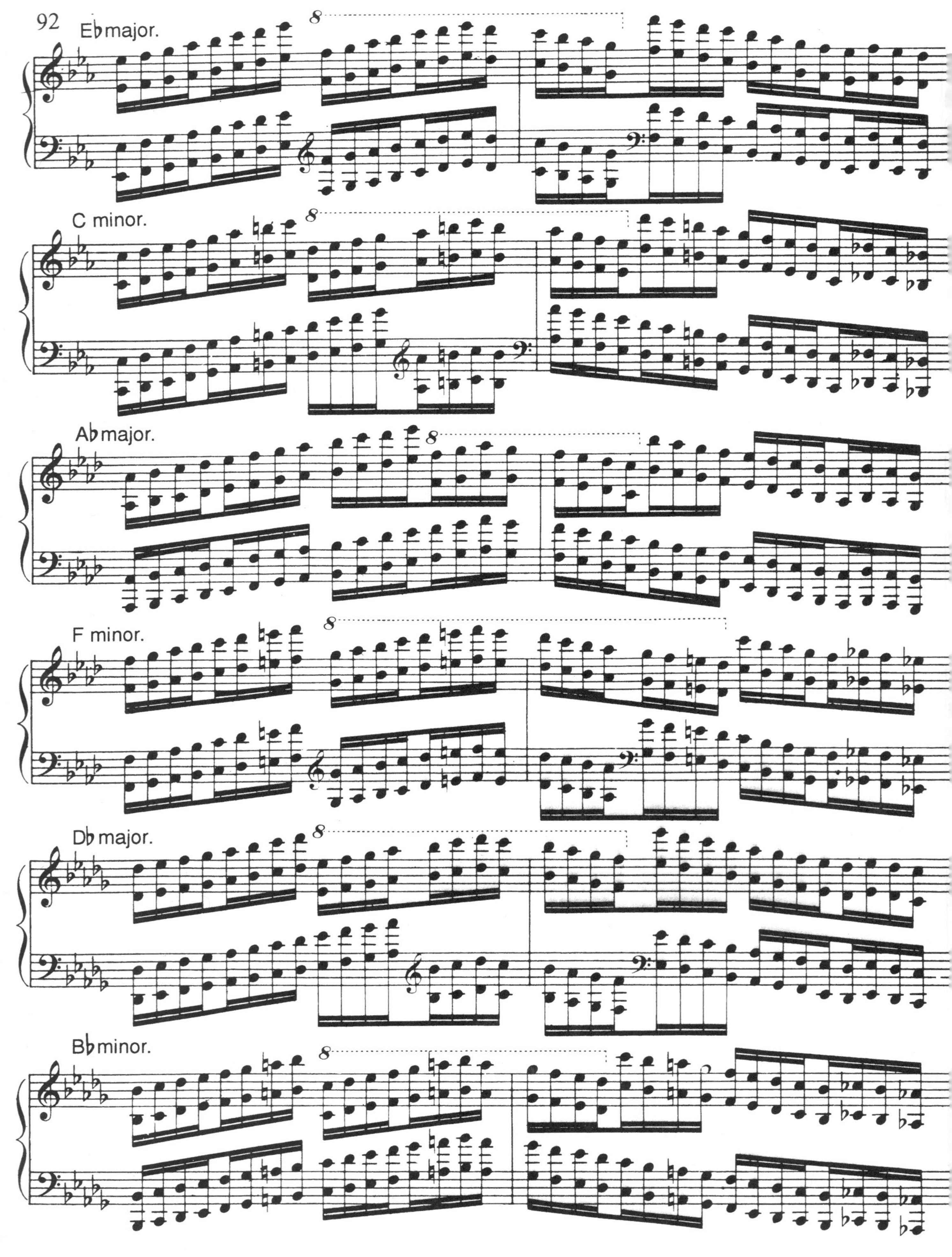
E♭ major.
C minor.
A♭ major.
F minor.
D♭ major.
B♭ minor.

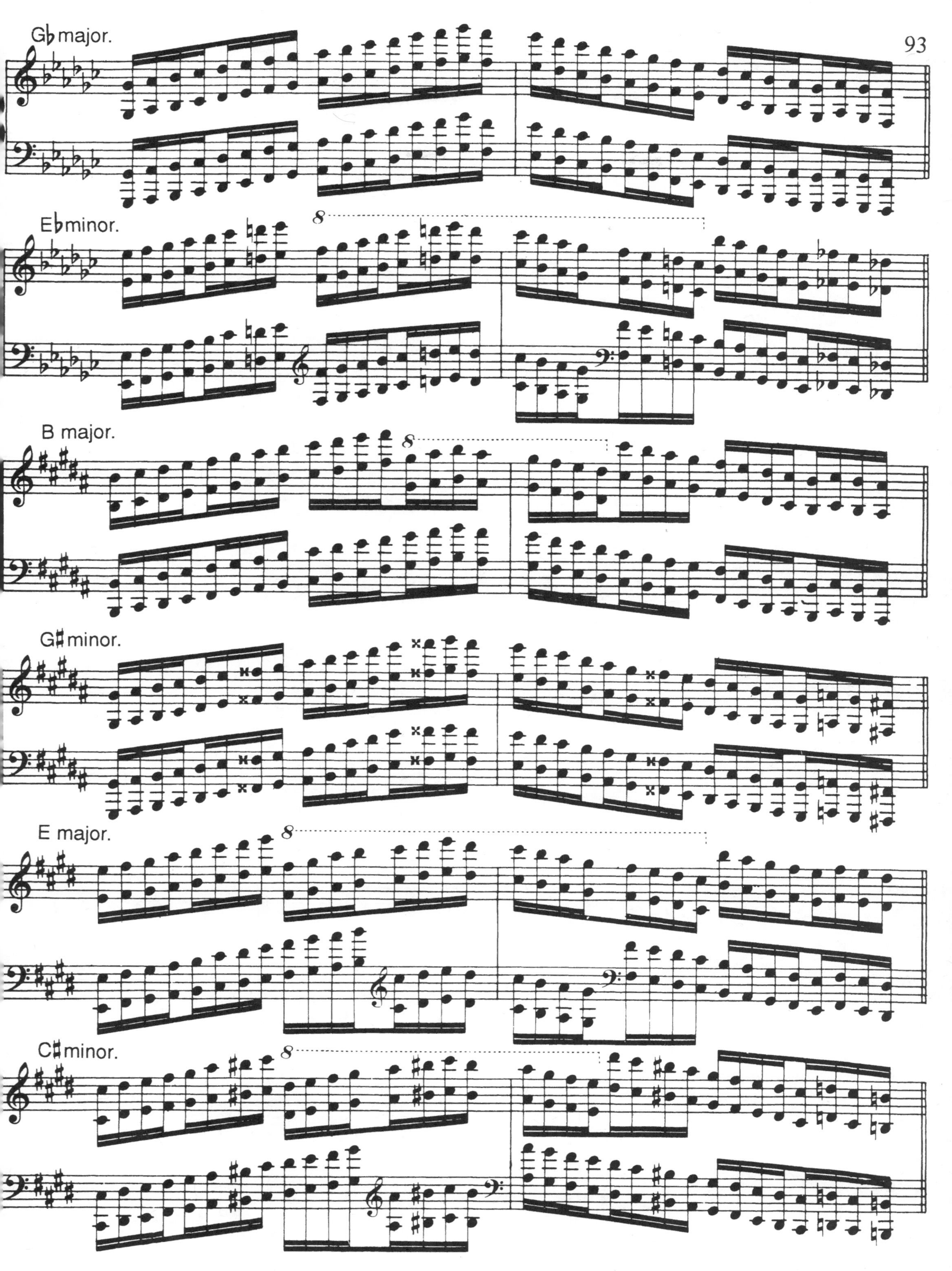
G♭ major.
E♭ minor.
8
B major.
8
G♯ minor.
E major.
8
C♯ minor.
8

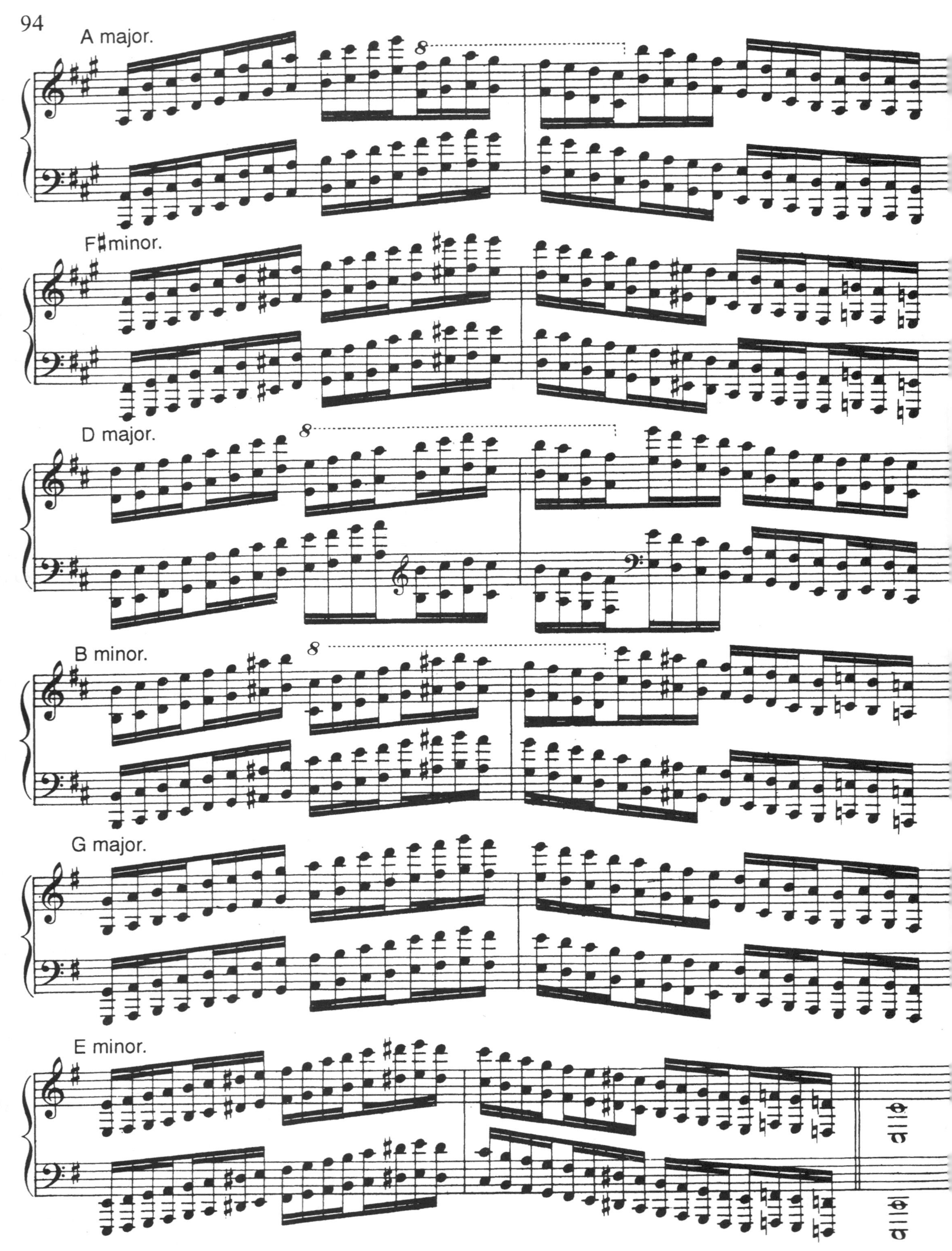
A major.
8
F♯minor.
D major.
8
B minor.
8
G major.
E minor.

The Fourfold Trill In Thirds, For All Five Fingers.

Maintain smoothness and evenness throughout this exercise, striking each third clearly.

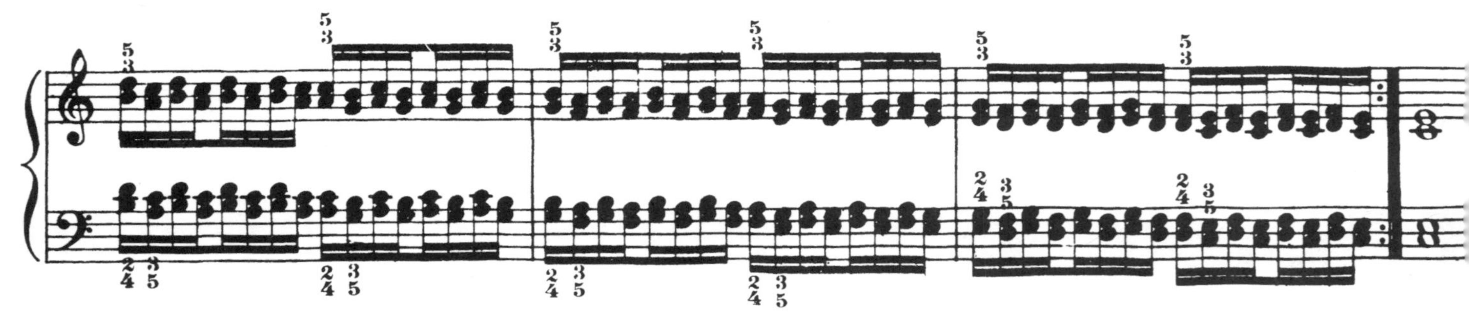

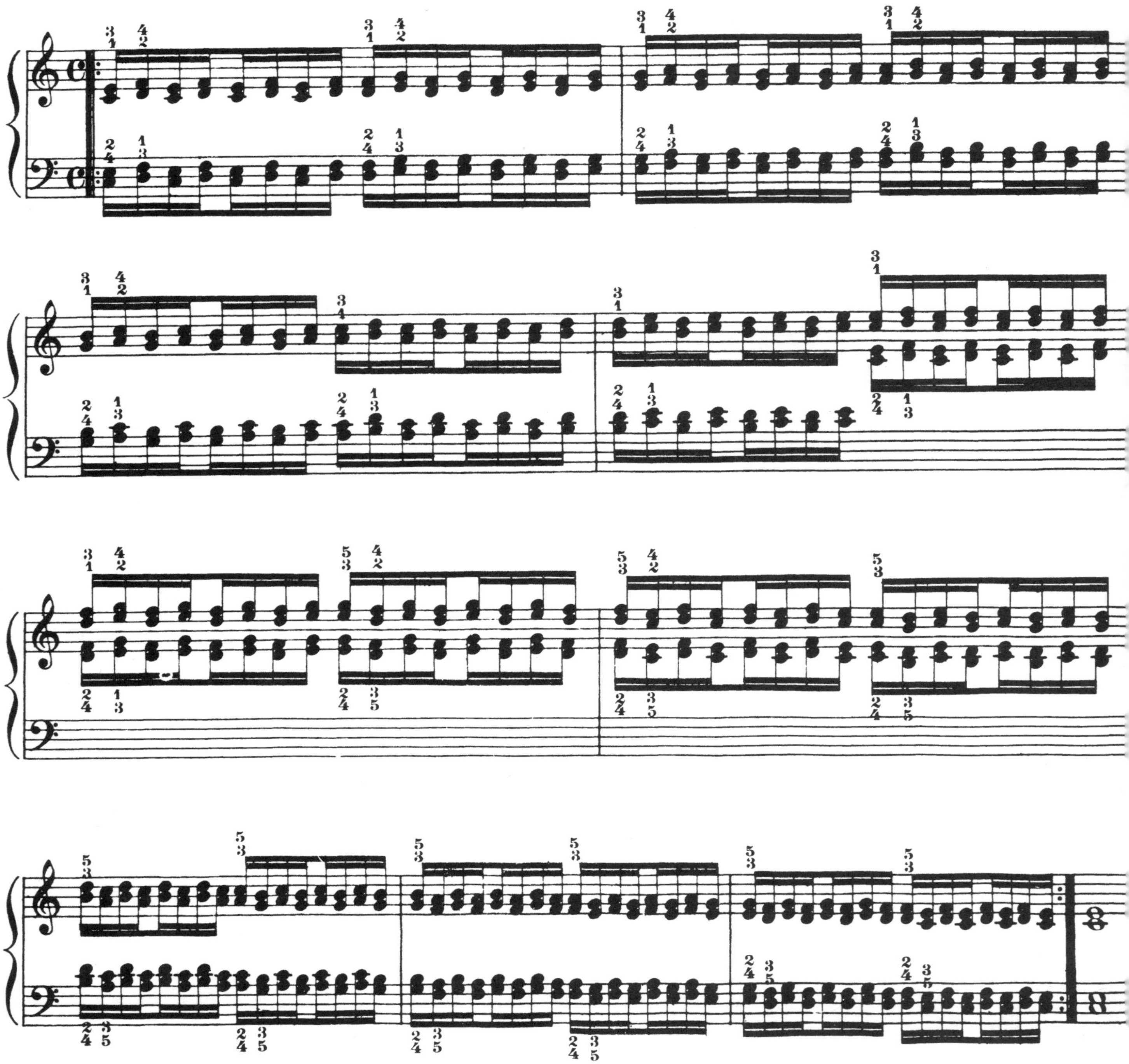

The Three Fold Trill.

See notes For Exercise No. 54

55.

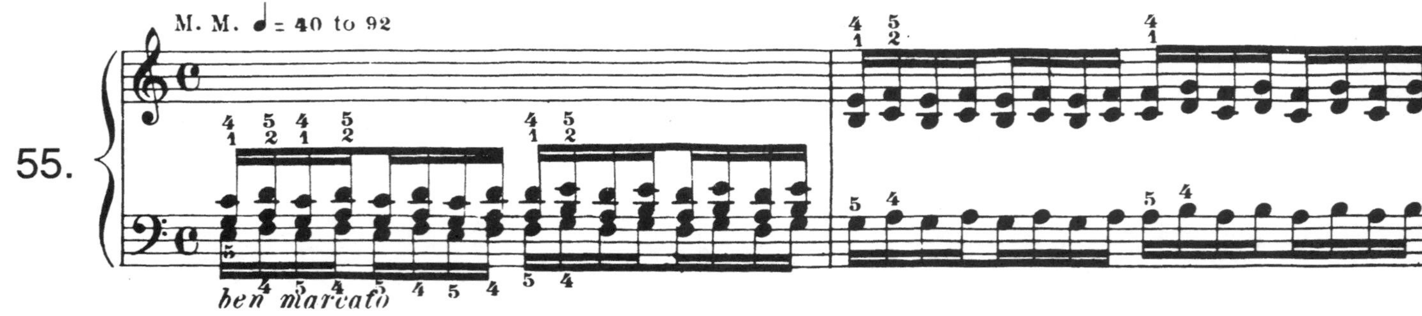

ben marcato

Special fingerings for the fourfold Trill.

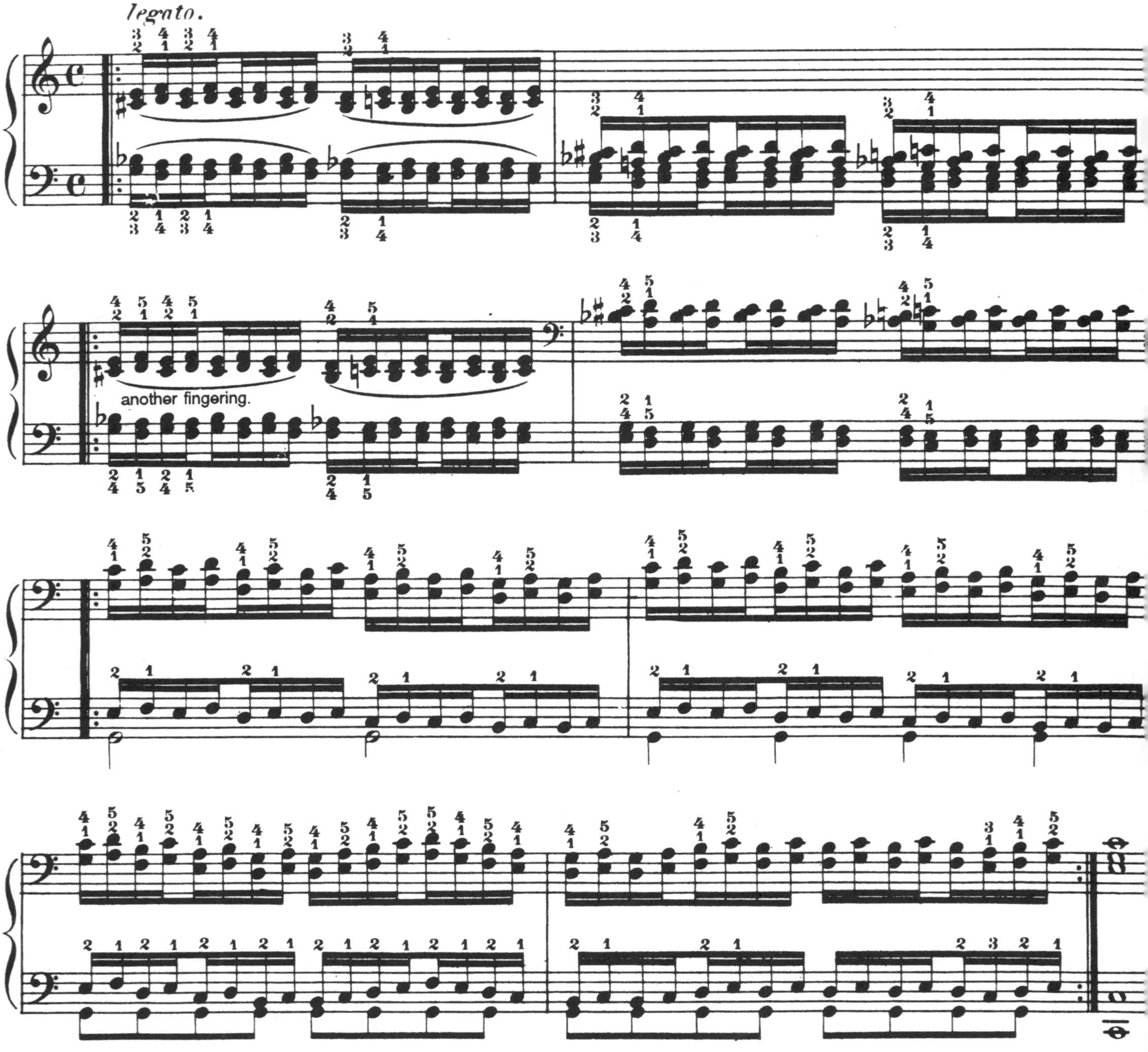

legato.

another fingering.

Scales in Broken Octaves, in the 24 Keys.

Play through each scale without stopping. Black keys should be played with the 4th finger of each hand. This exercise prepares the wrists for the study of tremolo.

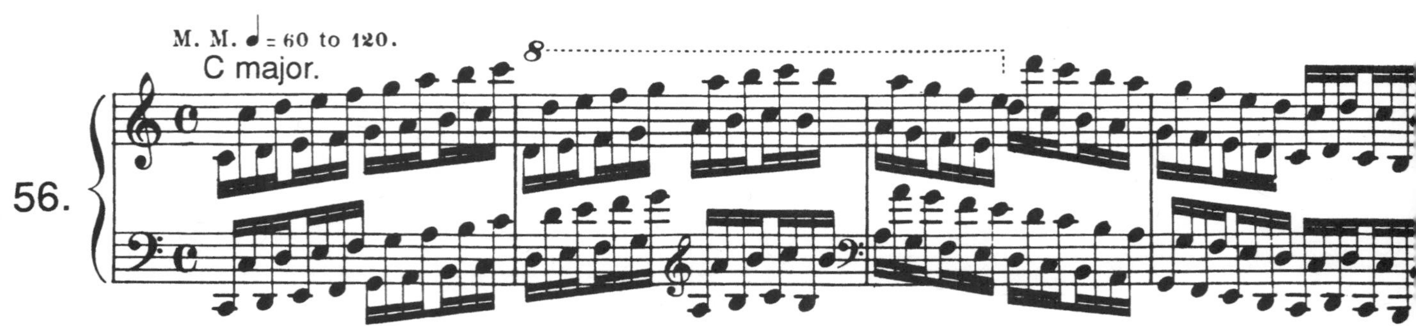

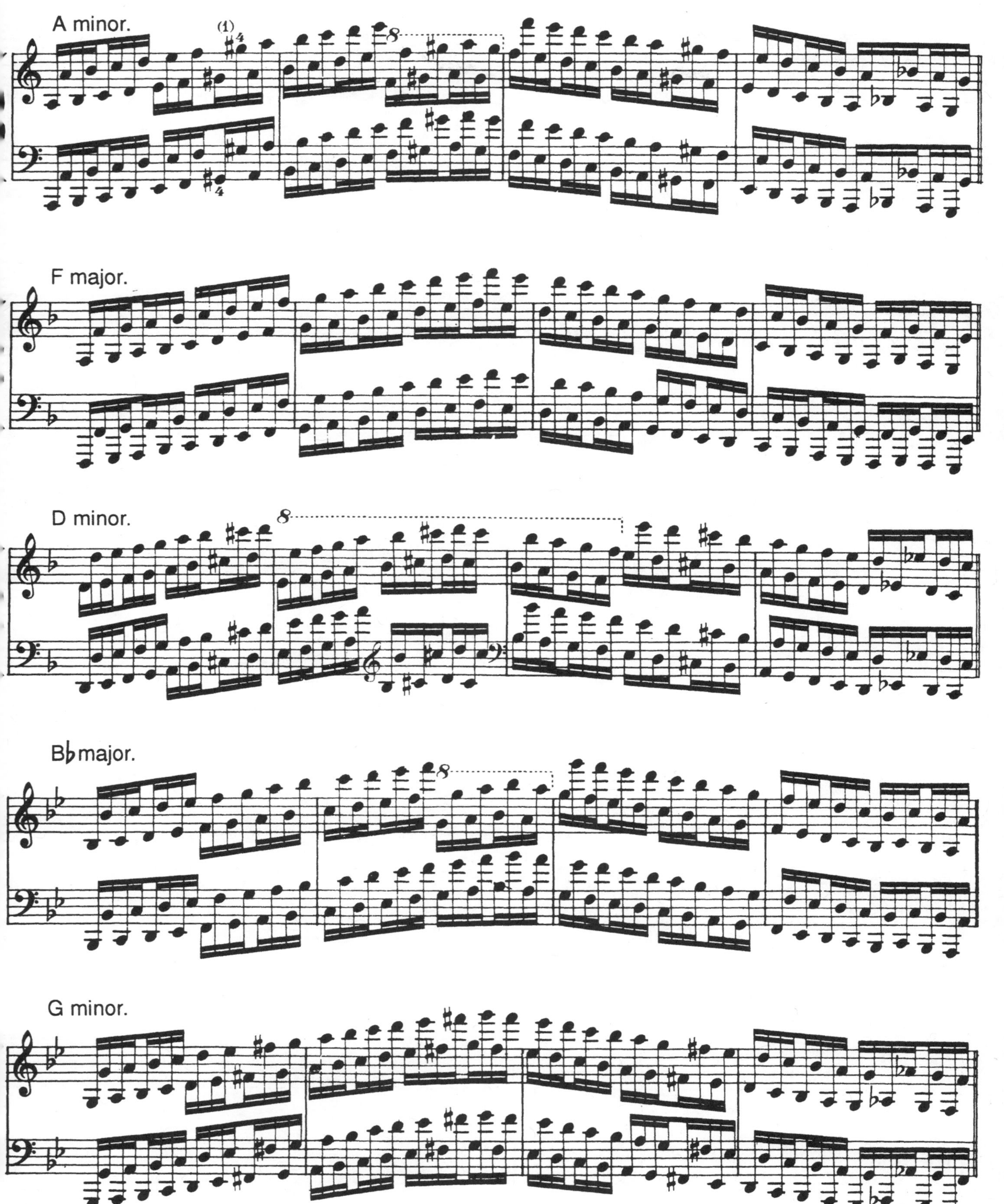
A minor.
(1)
4
8
4
F major.
D minor.
8
B♭ major.
8
G minor.

E♭ major.
8
C minor.
8
A♭ major.
8
F minor.
8
D♭ major.
8
B♭ minor.
8

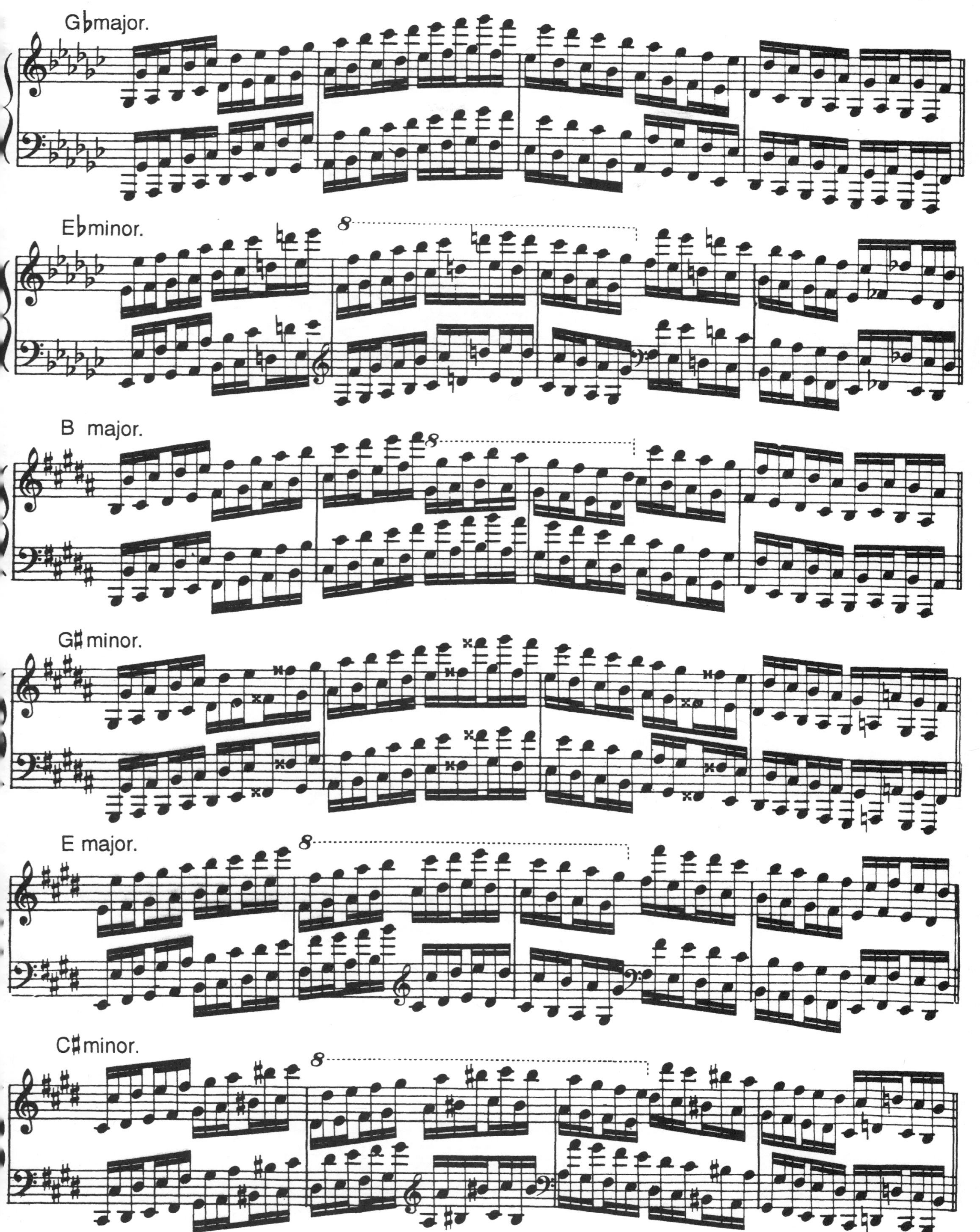
G♭major.
E♭minor.
8
B major.
8
G♯minor.
E major.
8
C♯minor.
8

A major.
F♯minor.
D major.
B minor.
G major.

Broken Arpeggios In Octaves In The 24 Keys.

Practice all arpeggios separately until they can be played very easily, then play the whole exercise without stopping. Maintain good wrist movement, playing cleanly and distinctly. Black keys may be played with the 4th finger of either hand. However, on the arpeggios of B major and E minor, on the following page are entirely on black keys, either the fourth or fifth finger can be used.

M. M. ♩= 40 to 72

57.

C major. 8

A minor. (1) 4 (1) 4

F major. 8

D minor 8

B♭ major. 8

G minor.

E♭ major. 8

C minor. 8

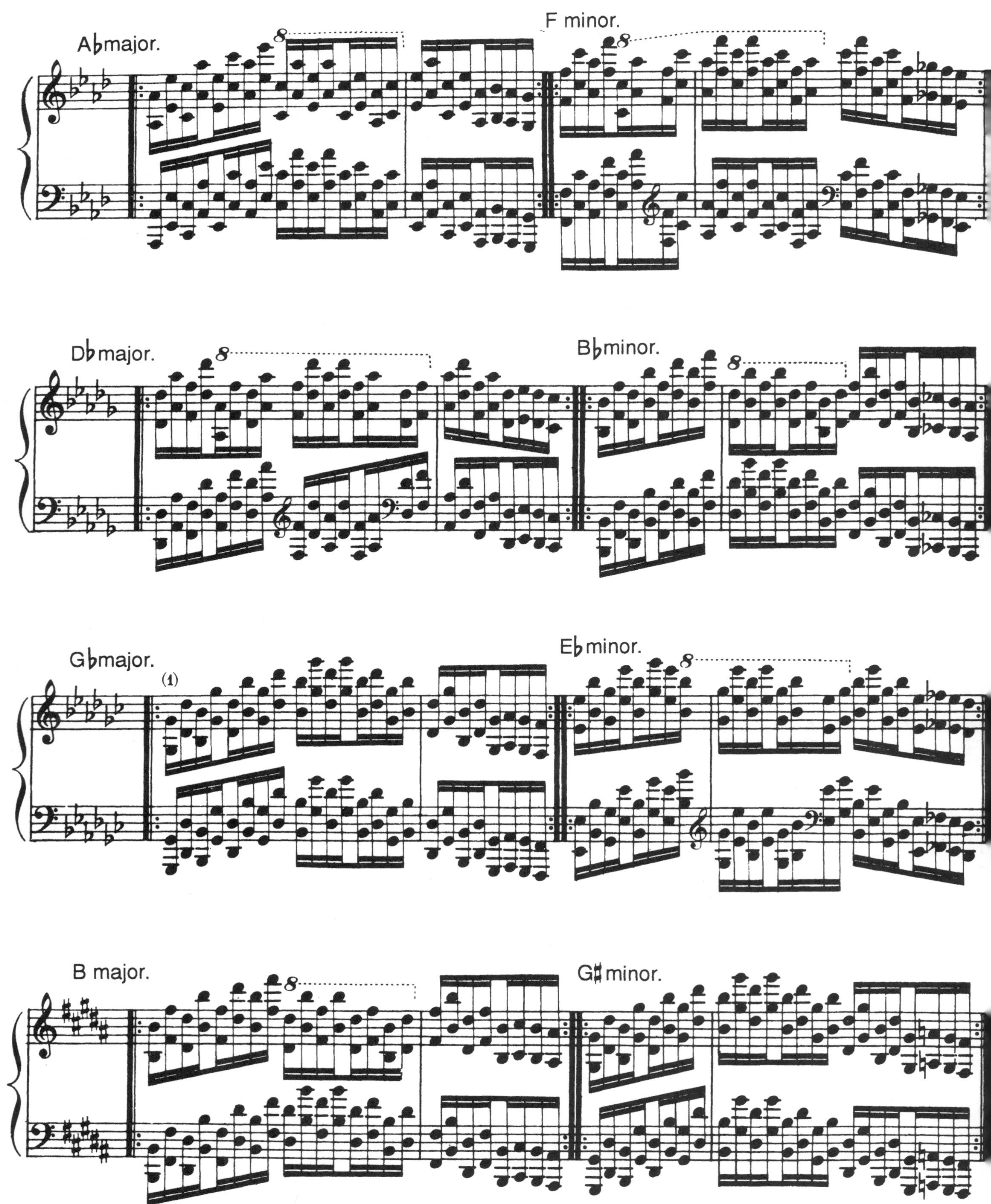
A♭major.
F minor.
D♭major.
B♭minor.
G♭major.
(1)
E♭minor.
B major.
G♯minor.

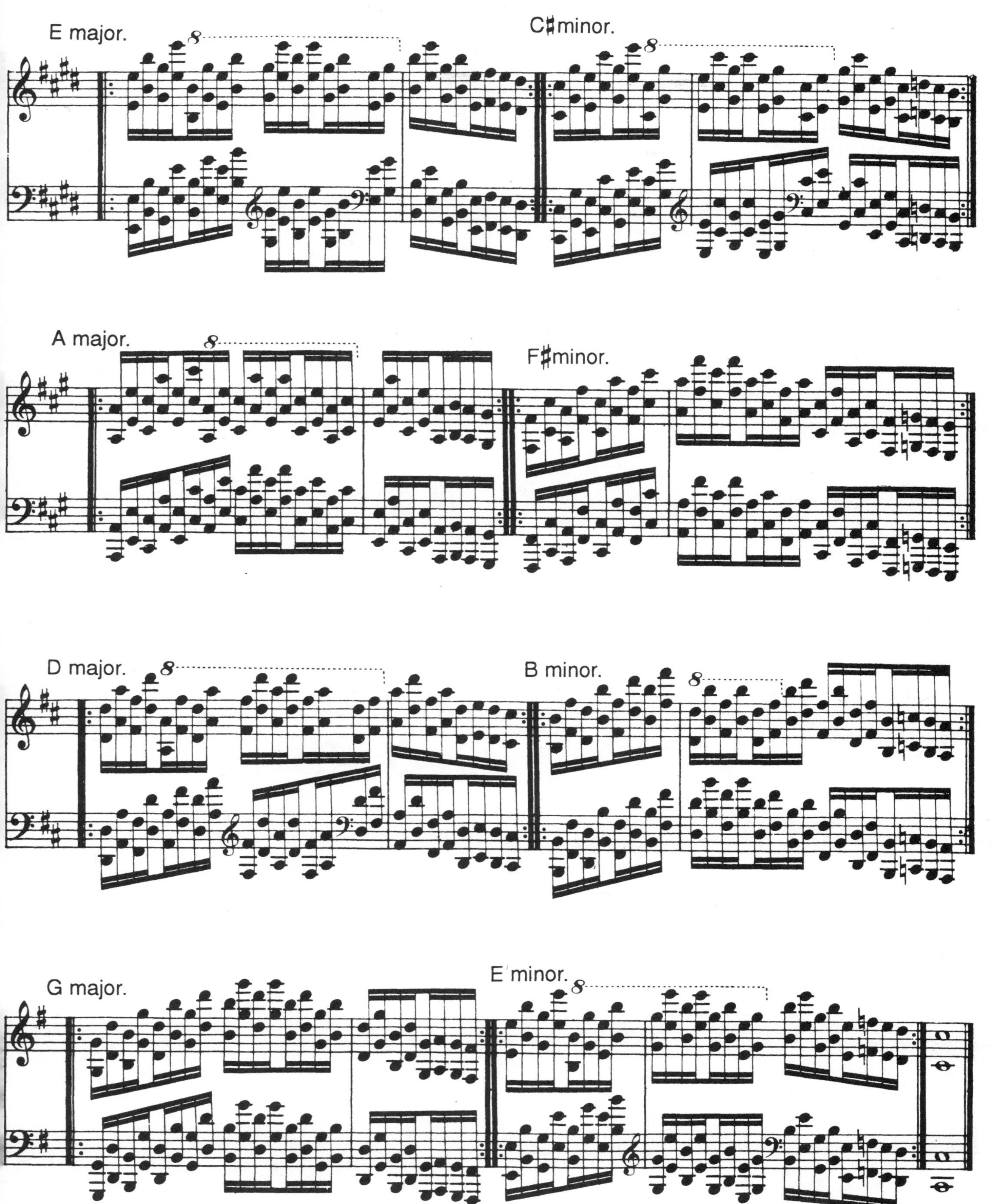
E major.
8
C♯minor.
8
A major.
8
F♯minor.
D major.
8
B minor.
8
G major.
E minor.
8

Sustained Octaves With Detached Notes.

Play the octaves vigorously without raising the wrists, and hold them down while playing the intermediate notes with a good finger movement.

8va bassa
8va bassa

Fourfold Trill In Sixths.

This exercise is for the combination of the 1st and 4th and 2nd and 5th fingers of each hand. All efforts should be made to keep the hands and wrists perfectly still.

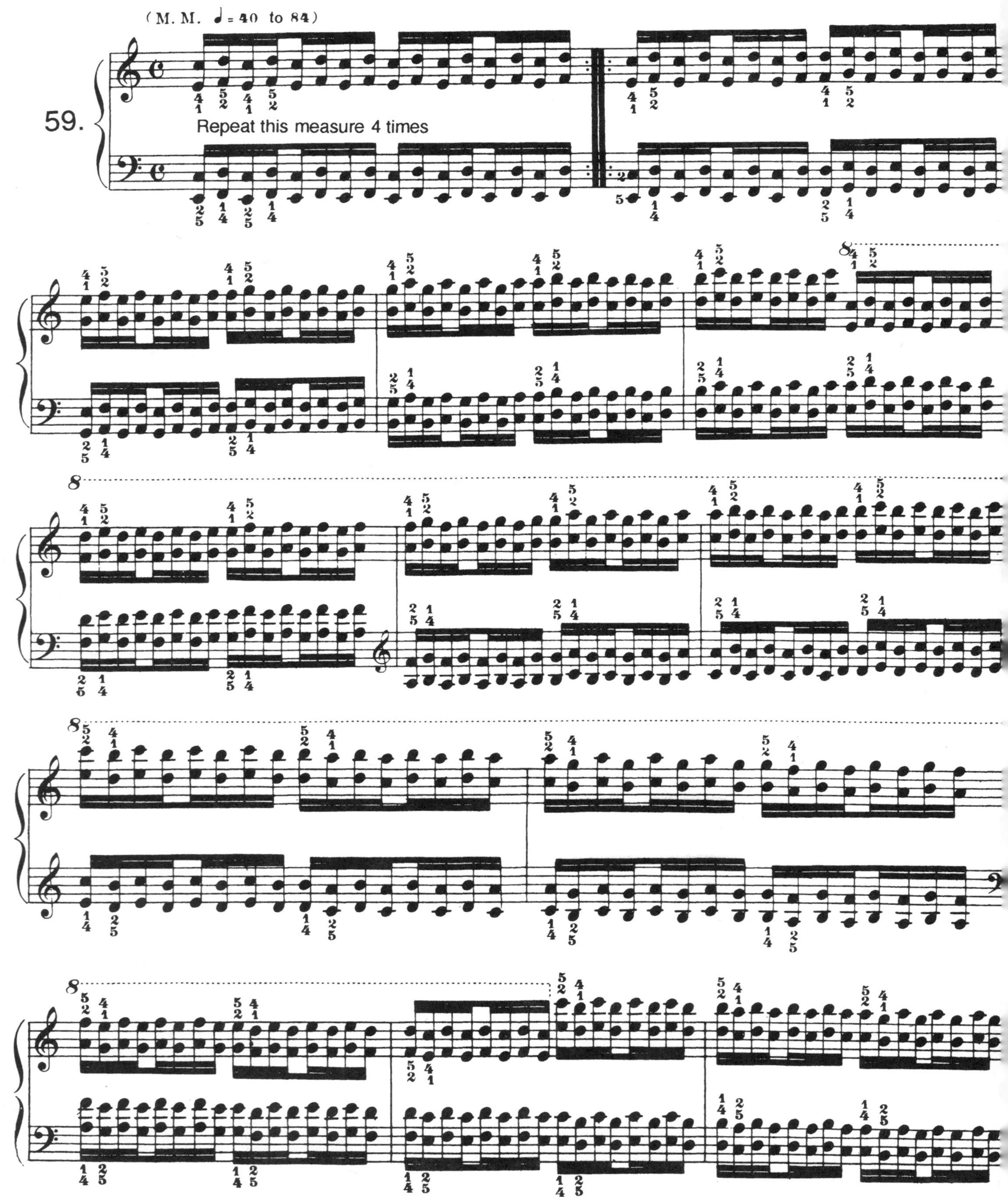

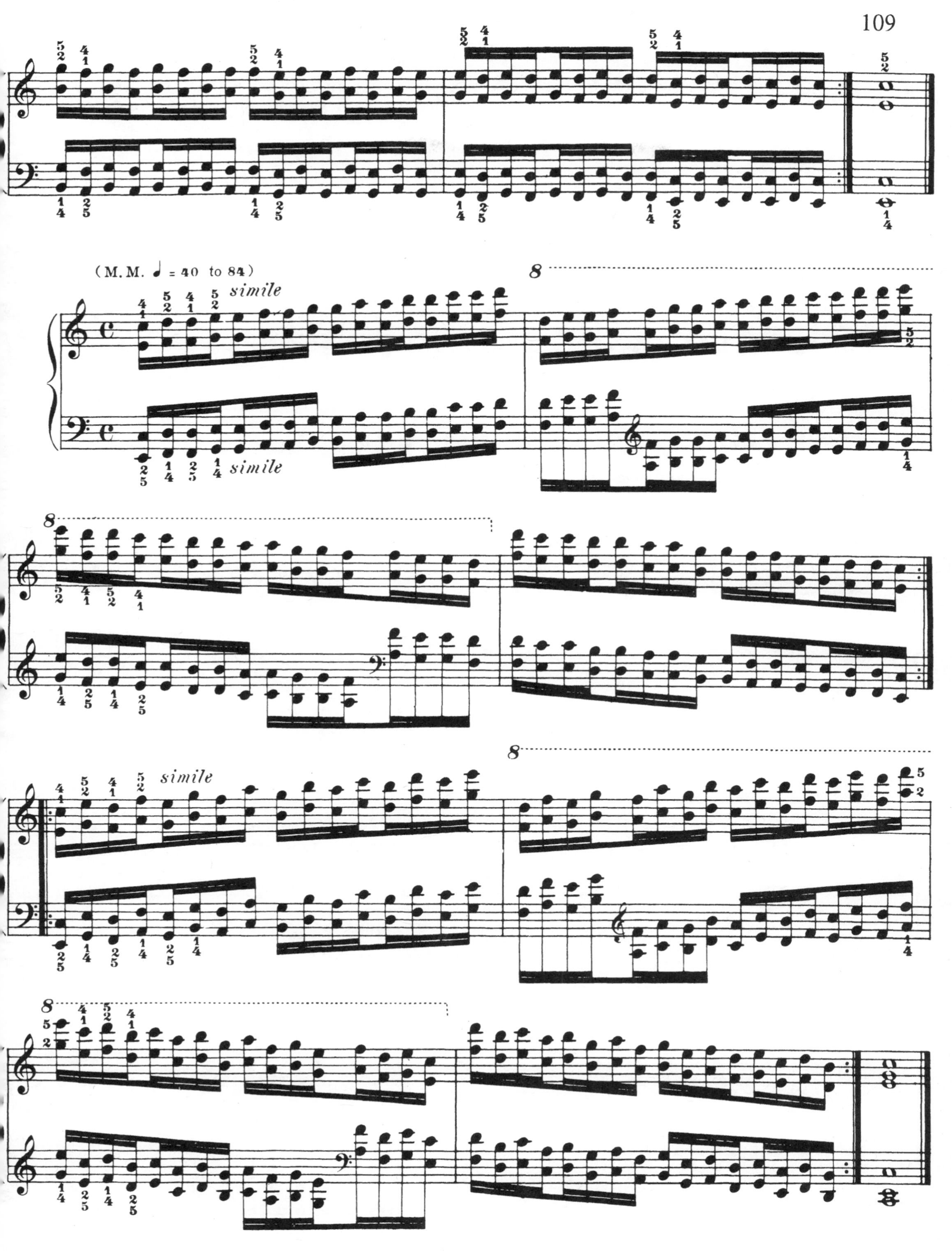
(M.M. ♩ = 40 to 84)
simile
simile
simile

The Tremolo.

Played properly the Tremolo should be as rapid as the roll on a drum. Practice slowly at first, gradually increasing the tempo to M.M.72. By allowing the wrists to turn rapidly from side to side, greater speed will be obtained. This exercise is long and difficult, but the excellent results will repay careful and persistent study. Steibelt made his listeners shiver by his execution of the tremolo.

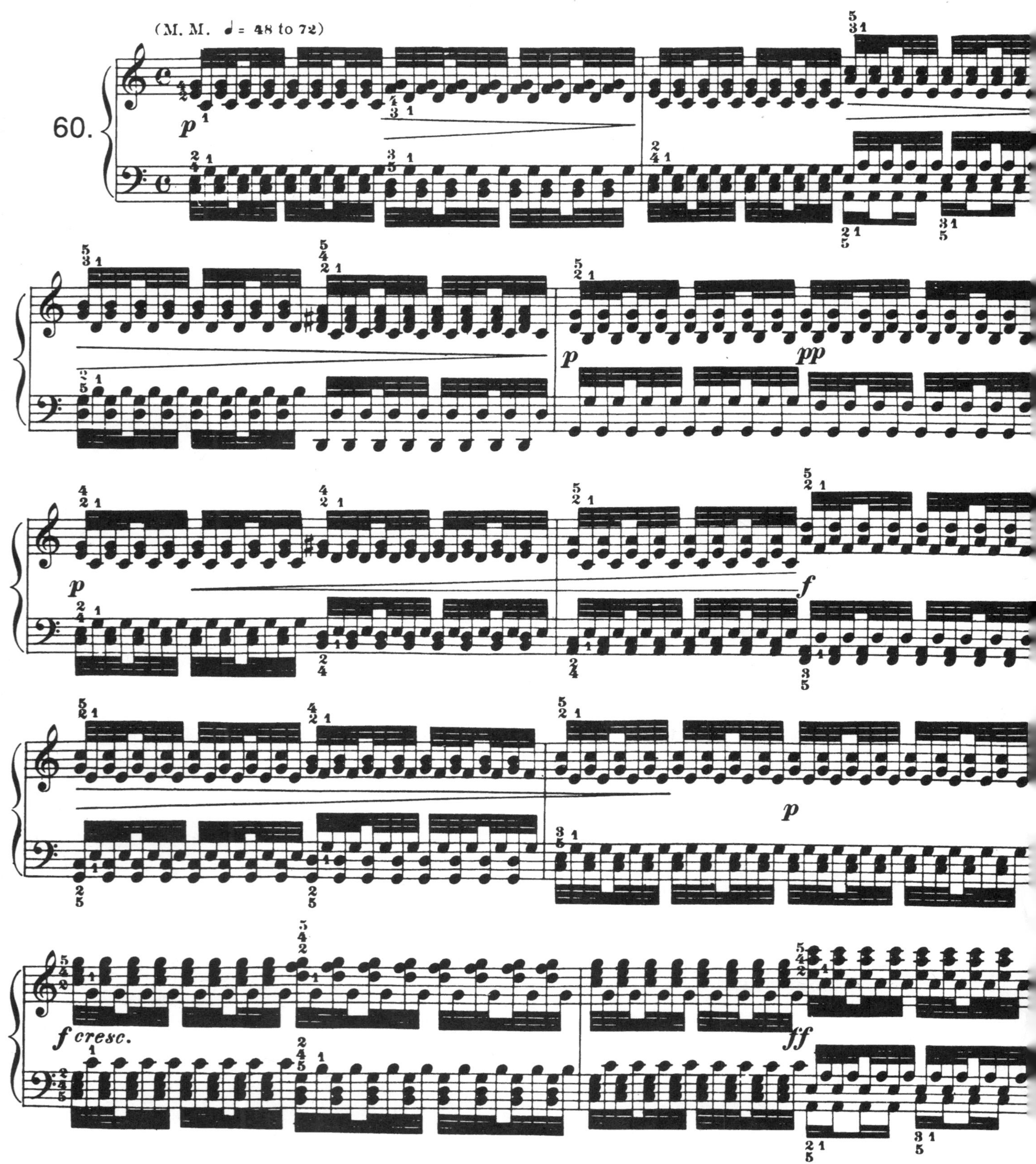

dim.
cresc.
f
ff
p
pp
p

p
cresc.
f
p
pp
cresc.
mf
pp
smorz.

p
poco rit.
a tempo pp
p
pp
perdendosi
8

dim.

Daniel Steibelt (1765 - 1823) was a German pianist and composer who was highly regarded in Europe during his lifetime.

End Of Part 3

After completing this book, the student should now be familiar with the most important technical difficulties in playing. To become a true virtuoso, the student should play through the entire book at least once a day, which will require one hour.

The great pianists repeat daily exercises for several hours, and the student aspiring to virtuosity must do the same.

The Best of Classics *for Intermediate Piano*

Best of Classics for Intermediate Piano is a comprehensive collection of intermediate to advanced piano solos that are essential recital standards for any accomplished pianist. These various works were chosen for their style, form, and for their suitability as recital performance pieces. This unique collection spans over two centuries and represents the masterworks of thirteen great composers: Bach, Mozart, Beethoven, Schubert, Schumann, Mendelssohn, Chopin, Tchaikovsky, Liszt, Brahms, Grieg, MacDowell, and Debussy. Each classic embodies the musical period in which they were written, Preludes & Fugues from the Baroque era, Sonatas & Variations from the Classical era, short pieces from the Romantic era, and transitional pieces from the Impressionistic period. Mastering these solos is an arduous task, but necessary as they are the core of any serious artist's repertoire.

___ TS275 • **Best of Classics for Intermediate Piano**

Best of Classical Themes *for Piano*

Best of Classical Themes published by Santorella Publications is a phenomenal resource for working musicians, as it contains a comprehensive index of most every Classical theme ever written by the greatest composers that ever aspired to dot ink on parchment or manuscript. This expansive encyclopedic musical reference guide has over 330 classic themes spanning over four centuries and representing over 100 composers. It is a must resource for every music student, educator, hobbyist, or historian. From Sousa's majestic march melodies to Chopin's magnificent mazurkas, this best-selling collection has it all. Written in a simple "*fake-book*" style fashion with chord symbols, is not only appropriate for piano, but also suitable for any melodic instrument. This enormous publication of classical themes is a one of a kind collection and a vital addition to any, every, and all personal music libraries.

___ TS276 • **Best of Classical Themes for Piano**

Debussy's *Claire de Lune & Reverie*
for Piano with Performance CD

Claude Debussy's Clair de Lune & Rêverie, transcribed and arranged by *Jonathon Robbins*, is available in two different editions. Both the Un-edited "*Concert Original*" as well as the "*Early Intermediate Edition*" are perfect for recitals, auditions, or performances. Each edition includes a performance recording which reveals the exceptional display of talent possessed by Debussy and the stylistic impact he had in moving the Romantic Era towards Impressionism.

Debussy was inspired by Paul Verlaine's poem, "Clair de Lune." The quiet, rolling melody and contradictory rhythms speak to the dream-like images and feelings of melancholy that the poem evokes, while the more meditative Rêverie is indicative of Debussy's earlier work.

Debussy once said, "Music is made up of colors and rhythms." No other pieces better exemplifies this than Clair de Lune & Rêverie. His use of melodic transition, arpeggios, dynamics & tempo creates a feast for the senses, and few composers have developed the use of texture like Debussy. Although he dedicated much of his life to Orchestral, Chamber & Operatic works, he also left an indelible mark with his compositions for piano. Clair de Lune and Rêverie are two highly significant compositions that embody the gradual evolution of the Romantic Era as it matured into period of Impressionism.

___ TS314 • **Late Beginner to Early Intermediate Edition for Piano**
___ TS315 • **Original "Unedited" Concert Performance Edition for Piano**

We Teach JAZZ PIANO

"Let's Play Jazz", is a complete method for learning piano. This beginning course has a unique approach. The student is taught, with a jazz influence from their very first lesson. From learning their first note to performing St. Louis Blues. The companion CDs will bring tons of fun to every session.

__TS286 • **Primer** __TS287 • **Book 1** __TS288 • **Book 2** __TS289 • **Book 3**
__TS399 • **Complete: Includes all four books in one shrink- wrapped package**

Jazz Piano Exercises & Etudes with CD Is the next step for the beginning jazzer, but don't stop there. Now is the time to advance your studies with two of the greatest books ever written for learning to play jazz piano chords. Jazz Chord Voicings for the Right Hand and Chord Voicings for Two Hands will teach you all you need to know. This best-selling series is a winning hand!

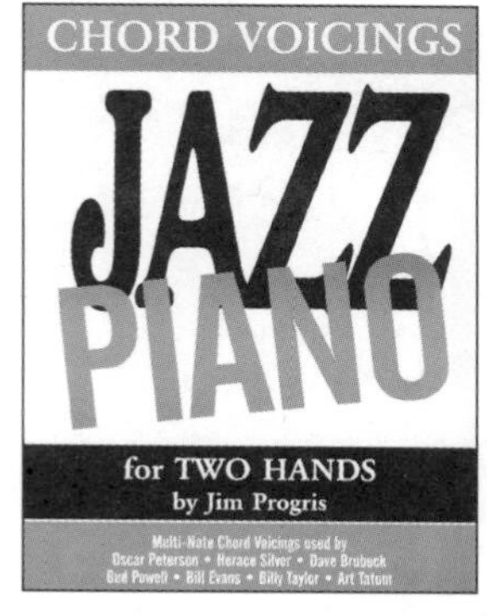

__TS065 • **Jazz Exercises & Etudes • Book 1**
__TS066 • **Jazz Exercises & Etudes • Book 2**
__LV019 • **Chord Voicings for Two Hands**
__LV020 • **Chord Voicings for the Right Hand**

Let's Play JAZZ PIANO!

Jazz Piano Cocktails and Creative Jazz Arranging contains some of the most incredible arrangements you have probably ever seen and quite possibly ever heard. Here's a great chance to spice up your repertoire. Classics to Jazz is one of our most challenging jazz titles, but playing them daily will keep your chops in tip-top shape.

__TS291 **Jazz Piano Cocktails with CD • Volume 1**
After You've Gone • Ain't She Sweet • You Made Me Love You • Limehouse Blues Poor Butterfly • It Had to Be You • Avalon • St. Louis Blues • I'm Confessin' and more.

__TS292 **Jazz Piano Cocktails with CD • Volume 2**
Chicago • Frankie & Johnnie • Sugar Blues • Tico Tico • Charleston • 12th St. Rag St. James Infirmary • Second Hand Rose • Oh, You Beautiful Doll and many more.

__TS293 **Jazz Piano Cocktails with CD • Volume 3**
Bye Bye Blackbird • Yes Sir, That's My Baby • Happy Days • Bill Bailey • Margie The One I Love • Amapola • Marie Elena • Ma, He's Making Eyes At Me and more.

__TS294 **Jazz Piano Cocktails with CD • Volume 4**
Alexander's Ragtime Band • Aba Daba Honeymoon • The Robert E. Lee • America Shimmy Like My Sister Kate • Barbados • The Japanese Sandman and many more.

__TS298 **Jazz Piano Cocktails with CD • Christmas Edition**
Jingle Bells • Deck the Halls • Jingle Bell Rock • Silver & Gold • Joy to the World Have A Holly Jolly Christmas • Rudolph, the Red-Nosed Reindeer and many more.

__TS290 **Jazz Piano Cocktails • Complete "Highlights" Edition**
This 208 page collection contains 55 memorable jazz classics as well as a salute to Scott Joplin, the King Of Ragtime who single handedly solidified the Ragtime Era

__TS154 **Classics to Jazz with CD • Complete "Highlights" Edition**
Classics to Jazz exercises & studies, derived from the original works of J.S. Bach, Mozart, Hanon & Czerny. Classic presented 1st, jazz rendition 2nd. In a word, Amazing!

__TS236 **Creative Jazz Piano Arranging with CD • Method & Songbook**
When Sunny Gets Blue • Days of Wine & Roses • Nearness of You • My Romance Georgia on My Mind • Hello Young Lovers • Sweet Georgia Brown • I Got it Bad Don't Blame Me • Don't Get Around Much Anymore • When I Fall in Love and more.

Beethoven's Greatest Sonatas

TRANSCRIBED ORIGINAL EDITIONS
INCLUDE PERFORMANCE CDS

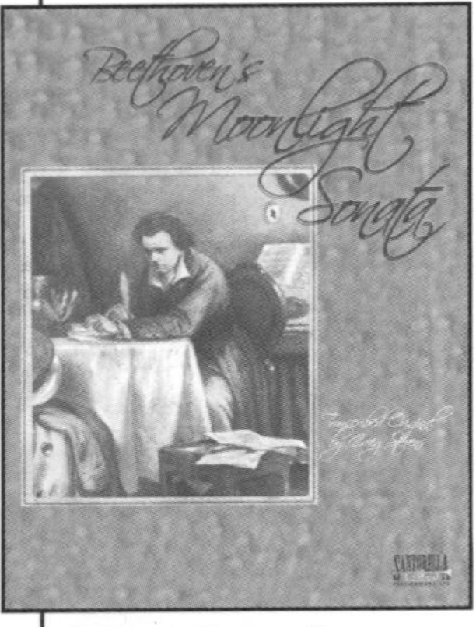

Moonlight Sonata
__TS340

Moonlight Sonata

Quasi Una Fantasia Opus 27, No.2, commonly known as the Moonlight Sonata, was dedicated to Beethoven's student, Countess Giulietta Guicciardi. She was only 17, yet Ludwig fell deeply in love. The piece was published by Cappa in 1802.

The title was suggested by poet Ludwig Rellstab. After hearing the piece, he had envisioned a boat on the waters of Lake Lucerne lit by the moonlight. Since then, it became known as the Moonlight Sonata, one of Beethoven's most celebrated works.

Sonata Pathetique

Grande Sonate Pathetique, Opus 13 in C Minor, was composed in 1798. This is the first of the 32 sonatas Beethoven wrote that acquired universal popularity. The much loved classic has been equally admired in esoteric and popular circles alike.

Dedicated to Prince Karl von Lichnowsky, the work, with its recurring tragic sonorities, embodies both passion and maturity. Some scholars have suggested that the piece's broad mix of influences may have included one of Mozart's later sonatas.

Sonata Pathetique
__TS341

Appassionata Sonata
__TS342

Appassionata Sonata

Dedicated to Count Franz Brunsvik, the Appassionata, in F Minor, Opus 57, was written in 1805 and published in 1807.

The title personifies the turbulent nature of this dramatic work. It contains driving rhythms, followed by a slow movement, culminating in a relentlessly powerful finale. One stormy evening, Beethoven clutched his manuscript and fled after an argument with Prince Lichnowsky. This original watermarked manuscript can be seen at the Bibliotheque Nationale in Paris.

Waldstein Sonata

Sonata in C Major, Opus 53, known as the Waldstein, was composed in 1804. The work was dedicated to Count von Waldstein, one of Beethoven's biggest influences and early financial supporters.

His gratitude towards Waldstein is quite apparent, as Beethoven expanded the limits of the sonata form in this, the first of his truly grand sonatas. Catering to neither the amateur nor the professional, Beethoven intended this work to be a superior, technically challenging sonata.

Waldstein Sonata
__TS343

Les Adieux Sonata
__TS344

Les Adieux Sonata

Sonata in E Flat Major, Opus 81A, known as Les Adieux, was composed between 1809 and 1810. It is one of two sonatas that Beethoven actually entitled, the other being the Sonata Pathetique.

Beethoven's dedication read, "On the departure of his royal highness, the esteemed Archduke Rudolf." Published in 1811, the sonata musically depicts the departure of the Archduke and the entire Imperial Family as they fled Vienna during the French bombardment in 1809.

Greatest Sonatas

For over 200 years Beethoven's sonatas have set the standard of excellence in solo piano composition. This collection includes transcribed originals of the best movements from five of the most important piano works ever written, Moonlight Sonata, Sonata Pathetique, Appassionata, Waldstein & Les Adieux.

Beethoven's use of phrasing, voicing, harmony, and technical challenges make these compositions the standard against which all piano literature is measured.

Greatest Sonatas
__TS345

Ethnic Favorites for Easy Piano

from Santorella Publications

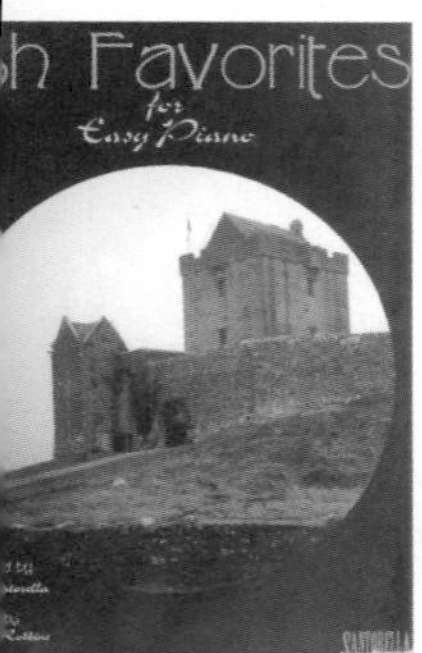

Irish Favorites for Easy Piano

__TS121

ALL LYRICS IN ENGLISH

Danny Boy • Kerry Dance • The Galway Piper Cockles and Mussels • Irish Eyes Are Smiling Come Back to Erin • The Irish Washerwoman Sweet Rosie O'Grady • Tourelay and more.

Italian Favorites for Easy Piano

__TS122

ALL LYRICS IN ITALIAN & ENGLISH

Funiculi - Funicula • O Sole Mio • Ah! Mari! Torna A Sorrento • Addio A Napoli • Tarantella Santa Lucia • Serenade • Carnival of Venice La Donna E'Mobile • Marcia Reale and more.

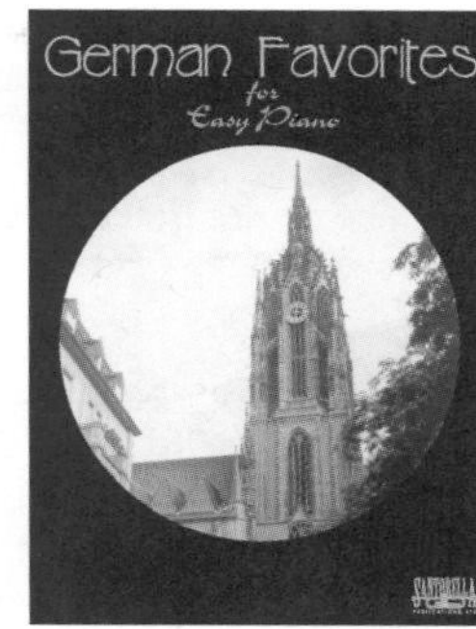

German Favorites for Easy Piano

__TS123

ALL LYRICS IN GERMAN

Von Meinem Bergli Muß Ich Scheiden • Drei Lilien Ö Freut Euch Des Lebens • Ein Prosit Der Gemütlichkeit • Schwarzbraun Ist Die Haselnuß • Heidschi Bumbeidschi and more...

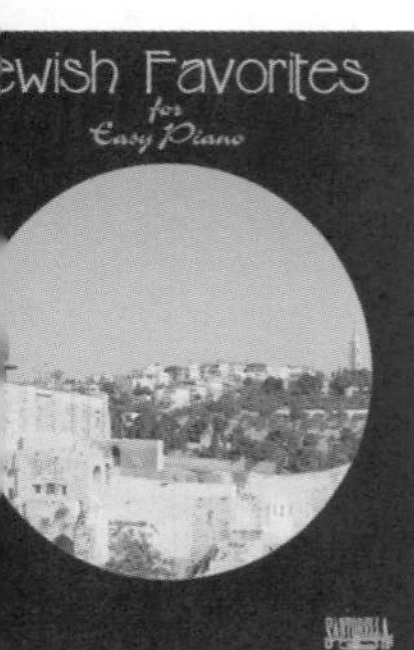

Jewish Favorites for Easy Piano

__TS124

ALL LYRICS IN HEBREW

Hava Nagila • Adir Hu • Adon Olam • Hatikva Avinu Malkenu • Ayri Kaylohaynu • Daiyenu Bahar Bagai • Eliyahu Hanavi • Chag Purim Shalom Aleychem • Oy Hanukkah and more...

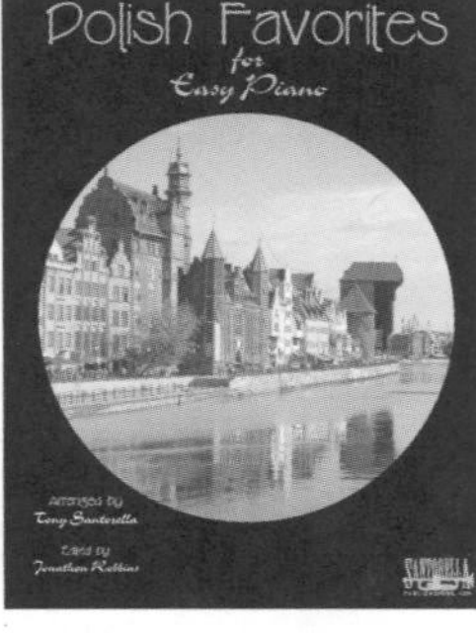

Polish Favorites for Easy Piano

__TS125

ALL LYRICS IN POLISH & ENGLISH

Annie Did It Wrong • Circus Polka • America Coal Miner's Polka • The Blonde Bombshell Who Stole the Keeshka? • Boom Chick-Chick Anniversary Waltz • Bridal Chorus and more...

Russian Favorites for Easy Piano

__TS126

ALL LYRICS IN RUSSIAN

Song of the Volga Boatmen (Ey Oochnyem!) Dark Eyes • Kaleenka • Farewell (Proshtchai) I Sing No More • Oh, Console Me! (Pozhaliey!) Ach Zatchem Eta Notch • Bublitchki and more.

Greek Favorites for Easy Piano

__TS127

ALL LYRICS IN GREEK

Saranta Palikaria • O Menussis • Susta Kritis Su Ipa Mana M' Pantrepse Me • Samiotissa Me Tis Elies • Makedonia Ksakusti • Karaguna Rovas Kotsari • Thalassaki Mou and more...

French Favorites for Easy Piano

__TS128

ALL LYRICS IN FRENCH

Ah! Vous Dirai-Je, Maman • Frère Jacques Au Claire de la Lune • Fais Dodo • Farandole Gymnopedie • La Marseilles • Skater's Waltz O Canada • Vive la Compagnie and more...

Latin Favorites for Easy Piano

__TS166

ALL LYRICS IN SPANISH

Adios Muchachos • Cielito Lindo • El Choclo Cose, Cose, Cose • El Relicario • Estrellita La Cumparsita • La Cucaracha • La Paloma Rico Vacilon • La Golondrina and more...

SANTORELLA PUBLICATIONS • Post Office Box 60 • Danvers, MA 01923 • info@santopub.com • www.santopub.com

PIANO PERFECT

Teaching Materials

__ TS221 Encyclopedia of Musical Knowledge
__ TS220 Santorella's Dictionary of Musical Terms
__ TS265 Easy Hanon for the Beginning Pianist • Robbins
__ OEP50 Hanon Complete for Piano • Original 60 Exercises
__ LS40011 Scales and Arpeggios for the Intermediate Pianist
__ OEP45 Basic Scales, Chords, Arpeggios & Cadences for Piano

Manuscript

__ HM001 First Place Music Writing Book, 12 Stave Spiral
__ HM002 First Place Music Writing Book, 10 Stave Perforated
__ HM004 First Place Music Writing Book, 6 Stave Spiral Book
__ TS499 Santorella's 6 Stave Manuscript Book & Lesson Log
__ TS205 Keyboard Kids • 4 Stave Wide Line Manuscript Paper

Keyboard Kids

__ TS200 Keyboard Kids Workbook • Color Notes & Rhythms
__ TS201 Keyboard Kids Book 1
__ TS202 Keyboard Kids Book 2
__ TS203 Keyboard Kids • Complete Beginners Method
__ TS206 Keyboard Kids "QUIET 88" Reversible Keyboard Chart
__ TS224 Keyboard Kids Flashcards – Volume 1
__ TS225 Keyboard Kids Flashcards – Volume 2
__ TS226 Keyboard Kids Flashcards – Volume 3

Chord Books

__ OEP40 Basic Keyboard Chords
__ TS207 Basic Piano Chord Chart
__ 78473 Piano Picture Chords • Complete
__ 78474 Essential Piano Picture Chords
__ 78477 Beginner Piano Picture Chords

Ethnic

__ TS121 Irish Favorites for Easy Piano
__ TS122 Italian Favorites for Easy Piano
__ TS123 German Favorites for Easy Piano
__ TS124 Jewish Favorites for Easy Piano
__ TS125 Polish Favorites for Easy Piano
__ TS126 Russian Favorites for Easy Piano
__ TS127 Greek Favorites for Easy Piano
__ TS128 French Favorites for Easy Piano
__ TS166 Latin Favorites for Easy Piano

Classics

__ 78200 Favorite Piano Classics • Originals
__ MP3107 The Big Book Of Classics for Piano
__ TS020 Exceptional Classics for Piano, Book 1
__ TS028 Exceptional Classics for Piano, Book 2
__ TS095 Chopin Preludes with Performance CD
__ TS097 Clementi Sonatinas for Piano • Opus 36
__ TS275 Best Of Classics for Intermediate Piano
__ TS276 The Best Of Classical Themes for Piano

Easy Classics

__ TS346 First Teacher's Classics
__ MP1102 Easy Classical Themes
__ MP2102 More Easy Classical Themes
__ MP3104 Great Themes of the Baroque Era
__ MP3103 Great Themes of the Classical Era
__ MP3102 Great Themes of the Romantic Era
__ MP3106 The Big Book Of Classical Themes for Piano

Teach Yourself Piano & Keyboards

__ 78349 Teach Yourself Piano with CD
__ 75561 Teach Yourself Electronic Keyboard with CD

Spanish Piano & Keyboard

__ 78353 Ensenese A Tocar El Piano
__ 75562 Ensenese A Tocar El Teclado Electronico
__ 75576 El Teclado Electonico de la A a la Z

Collections

Popular

__ TS089 Patriotic Melodies • Piano Vocal Edition with CD
__ TS040 Nostalgic Broadway & Popular Standards with CD
__ TS140 Essential Jazz Standards Complete Edition with CD
__ TS105 101 Popular Songs for Easy Piano • Including Lyrics
__ TS204 101 Popular "**Three Chord**" Easy Favorites for Piano

Childrens

__ MP1101 Songs for Children • Volume 1
__ MP3101 Songs for Children • Volume 2
__ MP2101 Patriotic Songs for Easy Piano
__ MP3105 Childhood Favorites for Easy Piano
__ OEP111 Classic Children's Songs for Easy Piano
__ TS266 Holiday Harmony for Easy Piano with CD
__ TS180 "**83**" Classified Easy Piano Solos with CD

Wedding & Sacred

__ TS059 "**22**" Sacred Gems for Piano
__ JT51 Elegant Wedding Classics for Piano
__ TS271 Best of Sacred • Piano Vocal Edition __ with CD
__ TS272 Best of Sacred • Organ Vocal Edition __ with CD
__ TS273 Best of Wedding • Organ Vocal Edition __ with CD
__ TS274 Best of Wedding • Piano Vocal Edition __ with CD
__ TS058 Promises Wedding Classics for Piano __ with CD

Easy Sacred

__ OEP103 Cherished Hymn Favorites
__ MP1226 Favorite Hymns for Easy Piano

Let's Play Jazz & More

Beginners Guide to Jazz Piano

__ TS286 Let's Play Jazz - Primer with CD
__ TS287 Let's Play Jazz - Book 1 with CD
__ TS288 Let's Play Jazz - Book 2 with CD
__ TS289 Let's Play Jazz - Book 3 with CD • Blues
__ TS399 Let's Play Jazz • Complete Method

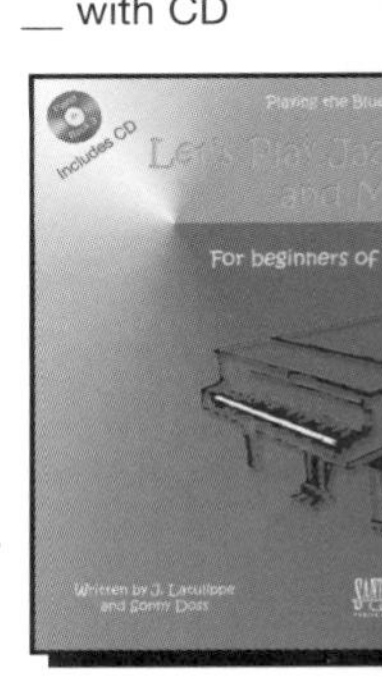

Jazz Piano • with CD

__ LV019 Jazz Chord Voicings for Two Hands • Progris
__ LV020 Jazz Chord Voicings for the Right Hand • Progris
__ TS045 Joplin's Greatest Rags • Original Edition with CD
__ TS048 Joplin's Greatest Rags • Easy Jazz Piano with CD
__ TS065 Jazz Piano Exercises & Etudes • Volume 1 with CD
__ TS066 Jazz Piano Exercises & Etudes • Volume 2 with CD
__ TS150 Classics to Jazz • Bach Edition (book only)
__ TS151 Classics to Jazz • Czerny Edition (book only)
__ TS152 Classics to Jazz • Hanon Edition (book only)
__ TS153 Classics to Jazz • Mozart Edition (book only)
__ TS154 Classics to Jazz • Complete Highlights with CD
__ TS290 Jazz Piano Cocktails • Complete Highlight Edition
__ TS291 Jazz Piano Cocktails • Volume I __ with CD
__ TS292 Jazz Piano Cocktails • Volume II __ with CD
__ TS293 Jazz Piano Cocktails • Volume III __ with CD
__ TS294 Jazz Piano Cocktails • Volume IV __ with CD
__ TS298 Jazz Piano Cocktails • Christmas Edition __ with CD
__ TS236 Creative Jazz Piano Arranging for Real "**FAKE-BOOK**" Tunes
Jazz Piano Method & Songbook with Performance CD